2000　　　　1st Edi

[Some pencil ann

CW00923319

Reading Hardy's Landscapes

Michael Irwin

First published in Great Britain 2000 by
MACMILLAN PRESS LTD
Houndmills, Basingstoke, Hampshire RG21 6XS and London
Companies and representatives throughout the world

A catalogue record for this book is available from the British Library.

ISBN 0–333–74191–9

 First published in the United States of America 2000 by
ST. MARTIN'S PRESS, INC.,
Scholarly and Reference Division,
175 Fifth Avenue, New York, N.Y. 10010

ISBN 0–312–22403–6

Library of Congress Cataloging-in-Publication Data
Irwin, Michael, 1934–
Reading Hardy's landscapes / Michael Irwin.
p.   cm.
Includes bibliographical references (p.   ) and index.
ISBN 0–312–22403–6 (cloth)
1. Hardy, Thomas, 1840–1928—Technique.   2. Hardy, Thomas,
1840–1928—Settings.   3. Wessex (England)—In literature.
4. Landscape—England—Wessex.   5. Landscape in literature.
6. Description (Rhetoric)   7. Setting (Literature)   I. Title.
PR4757.L3I79   1999
823'.8—dc21
                                                    99–15880
                                                    CIP

© Michael Irwin 2000

All rights reserved. No reproduction, copy or transmission of this publication may be made without written permission.

No paragraph of this publication may be reproduced, copied or transmitted save with written permission or in accordance with the provisions of the Copyright, Designs and Patents Act 1988, or under the terms of any licence permitting limited copying issued by the Copyright Licensing Agency, 90 Tottenham Court Road, London W1P 0LP.

Any person who does any unauthorised act in relation to this publication may be liable to criminal prosecution and civil claims for damages.

The author has asserted his right to be identified as the author of this work in accordance with the Copyright, Designs and Patents Act 1988.

This book is printed on paper suitable for recycling and made from fully managed and sustained forest sources.

10   9   8   7   6   5   4   3   2   1
09   08   07   06   05   04   03   02   01   00

Printed and bound in Great Britain by
Antony Rowe Ltd, Chippenham, Wiltshire

Reading Hardy's Landscapes

Also by Michael Irwin

HENRY FIELDING: The Tentative Realist

PICTURING: Description and Illusion in the Nineteenth-Century Novel

STRIKER

WORKING ORDERS

Contents

List of Plates

Claude Lorrain, *Landscape with Hagar and the Angel* (reproduced by permission of National Gallery Publications Limited)

John Constable, *The Cornfield* (reproduced by permission of National Gallery Publications Limited)

John Constable, *The Leaping Horse* (reproduced by permission of the Royal Academy of Arts, London)

Medardo Rosso, *Laughing Woman* (reproduced by permission of Tate Gallery Publishing Limited)

Giorgio Morandi, *Natura Morta* (reproduced by permission of Museo Morandi)

Preface

The fundamental point

This book represents the coming together of two interests. One is specific: the work – especially the fiction – of Thomas Hardy. The other, more general, is the capacity of certain novelists to create the illusion of a physical world, with sights to see and sounds to hear.

The ability to bring a narrative to life in this way is too easily taken for granted. The set-piece description – of Count Fosco, or Egdon Heath, or Daniel Peggotty's boat – readily lends itself to critical 'appreciation'; but much of the pictorial power of a work of fiction is likely to derive from a succession of brief allusions, artfully distributed. Unobtrusive patterns of detail can conjure up vivid mental images – verbally-evoked faces, clothes, gestures, furnishings, buildings and streets.

When I wrote a book on this aspect of nineteenth-century English fiction Hardy featured prominently, as one of our great visualizers. Over a period of years, however, my response to this aspect of his work has broadened. I now see these descriptive passages as central to his fiction. What in other novelists is enabling matter, in Hardy's case becomes the dominant force. The human drama seems virtually to lose itself in the background, or rather dissolve into it, and yet to take on the more significance for doing so.

I will be arguing that the essential meaning of most of the novels must be traced to the tension and mutual dependency between background and characters, Landscape and Figures, either term capable – as will be seen – of absorbing, even annihilating, the other.

Hardy himself remarks:

'The world often feels certain works of genius to be great, without knowing why: hence it may be that particular poets and novelists may have had the wrong quality in them noticed and applauded as that which makes them great.' (*Life*, 117)

I considered using the comment as an epigraph to this book, but decided that it would be presumptuous to do so. There has been a great deal of critical writing about Hardy, and much of it has been thoughtful and illuminating. This book will be attempting not so much to supplant established readings, as to fold them into what I take to be a larger, more inclusive view. On occasion I will have to traverse fairly familiar ground in an attempt to explore beyond it. But I hope that the Hardy who emerges from this mode of analysis will seem a richer, more complex, more wide-ranging novelist than even his admirers have generally taken him to be.

This book derives from a Hardy course which I have taught at the University of Kent, originally alongside Ian Gregor. No collaborative enterprise could have been pleasanter. It is a tribute both to Hardy and to Ian that the course has remained so exhilarating, continuing to develop year after year. I learned more than I can say both from Ian and from our many alert and responsive students – in particular from Sarah Clark, my best student, some of whose ideas I have, with her consent, coolly purloined.

I would like to thank her, and also various friends with whom I have from time to time discussed aspects of the text – notably Keith Carabine and Nick Garland. Because my argument is to an extent idiosyncratic I happen to quote relatively little from the extensive Hardy criticism which I have read with pleasure and profit over the years. I am grateful to many a commentator whose name does not happen to figure in the pages that follow. The point is one I'd like to emphasize, because Hardy critics are a convivial and mutually supportive fraternity. The conferences at Dorchester, where some of the ideas in this book were first aired, are as enjoyable as they are educative. My last tribute goes to Jim Gibson, a friend for years in a variety of contexts. He and his wife, Helen, have done much to make these conferences the great occasions they have become.

MICHAEL IRWIN

References and Abbreviations

Page references relating to Hardy's novels are based on the World's Classics Edition (General Editor: Simon Gatrell) except as indicated below. Novel titles are abbreviated as shown.

DR   *Desperate Remedies (Macmillan: New Wessex pb.)*
FMC   *Far from the Madding Crowd*
HE   *The Hand of Ethelberta (Macmillan: New Wessex pb.)*
JO   *Jude the Obscure*
Lao   *A Laodicean*
MC   *The Mayor of Casterbridge*
PBE   *A Pair of Blue Eyes*
RN   *The Return of the Native*
Tess *Tess of the d'Urbervilles*
T-M   *The Trumpet-Major*
TT   *Two on a Tower*
UGT   *Under the Greenwood Tree*
W-B   *The Well-Beloved*
Wood *The Woodlanders*

Discussion of the short stories is based on the texts as edited by Norman Page in *The Complete Stories* (London: Dent pb., 1996). Exceptions are 'An Indiscretion in the Life of an Heiress' and 'Our Exploits at West Poley' (Macmillan: New Wessex edition of *The Stories of Thomas Hardy*, Volume Three, 1977, edited by F. B. Pinion).

Poems are quoted as from *The Complete Poems of Thomas Hardy*, edited by James Gibson (Macmillan, 1976).

Where *Life* is cited the reference is to *The Life and Work of Thomas Hardy*, edited by Michael Millgate (Macmillan, 1984).

Essays by Hardy are quoted as from *Thomas Hardy's Personal Writings*, edited by Harold Orel (Macmillan, 1967).

Quotations from *The Dynasts* are based on the Macmillan paperback edition of 1965.

1
Introduction

'That's what the name is *called*. The name really *is* "*The Aged Aged Man.*"'
'Then I ought to have said "That's what the *song* is called"?' Alice corrected herself.
'No, you oughtn't: that's quite another thing! The *song* is called "*Ways and Means*": but that's only what it's *called*, you know!'
'Well, what *is* the song, then?' said Alice, who was by this time completely bewildered.
'I was coming to that,' the Knight said. The song really *is* "*A-sitting On A Gate*" ...'[1]

An exhibition at the National Gallery in 1994, entitled 'Claude: the Poetic Landscape', was dedicated to rehabilitating the narrative aspect of the works displayed.[2] The aim was to refute the familiar criticism that the small, often ill-drawn, figures in Claude's paintings are a negligible aspect of his art, perhaps included merely as a reluctant concession to contemporary taste. It's easy to see why such a view should have become current. Frequently it is only the title of a given work which enables one to identify the unnoticeable human participants as (for example) Jacob, Laban and his daughters, or Aeneas and the Cumaean Sibyl. Claude was obviously a great landscape painter, but in his own day the genre was not held in high esteem, based, as it seemed to be, on 'mere' imitation of external realities. By contrast it was believed that a biblical, historical or mythological theme would stir the emotions and convey a message or moral. In such cases the landscape could subserve a story of sufficient grandeur, providing a setting appropriate in scale and mood. Its composition could direct the eye to essential features of the human drama. Moreover where the subject of the painting, the 'story' being illustrated, implied a theme, that theme might be echoed and developed in the scenic background, lending natural features an expressive significance which in themselves they could not have. A landscape without figures would be inert and unmeaning.

This view, with which Claude contended or colluded, has come to seem radically confused. Today the assumption would surely be that a portrayal of landscape alone not only can convey, but cannot avoid conveying, 'meaning', if of an indistinct kind. For example, any such painting will depict potentially antagonistic forces. Vegetation confronts weather. Trees may be flowering in sunshine or struggling against the wind. The sky may be a settled blue or a confusion of shifting clouds. Almost inevitably the artist seems to imply harmony, unease, change or turbulence. Distance offers a further dimension of possible significance: the scenery in the foreground, for example, may be in dramatic contrast to the vista beyond. Cultivation may be in a dialectic with wilderness. There may or may not be signs of human activity, past or current. The landscape may be dominated by a fortress or a cathedral; it may be re-absorbing the decaying remnants of a castle, a cottage or a bridge. Such depredation introduces the invisible 'figure' of Time, who might be glimpsed also in the falling of leaves or the setting of the sun. There is a sense in which Nature is continuous narrative, and any pictorial rendering of it is bound to tell a story.

Another figure inevitably present in the painting, though physically invisible, is that of the painter. This particular scene has been selected, this season of the year, this weather, this time of day: all such choices might be assumed to display the artist's taste, psychology, mood, view of life. The representation of an external world may be read as a reflection of a mental or spiritual world.

The viewer attempting to adjudicate between different possible readings of a landscape is likely to take a lead from the title of the painting. 'Moses and Aaron' implies a narrative interest; 'Landscape with Mountains and Waterfalls' puts the emphasis on scenic effect; 'The Land of Lost Content' might suggest alternatively a private recollection or a generalized exercise in nostalgia.

The painting we now know as 'The Cornfield' was first exhibited under the title 'Landscape', but was later referred to by Constable as the 'Drinking Boy'. The artist exhibited the work three more times, retitling it successively 'Paysage avec figures et animaux', 'Noon' and 'Harvest – Noon; a Lane Scene'.[3] If the title of a painting may be taken to indicate what it is 'about', these changes would seem to suggest confusion. Was Constable uncertain about the meaning of his own painting? In a letter he said that he been tackling 'a subject of a very different nature [from 'The Lock'] – inland – cornfields – a close lane – kind of thing – but it is not neglected in any part the trees are more than usually studied and the extremities well defined – as well as their species [?stems] – they are shaken by a pleasant and healthful breeze – *"at Noon" ...* '.[4] It might be suggested that Constable is here talking about 'subject-matter' rather than 'subject', listing the constituent elements of his picture rather than saying what it is to be 'about'. The entities alluded to in this letter and in the various titles duly feature in the completed work – landscape, people, animals, a lane, cornfields, a drinking boy. All are represented with care and affection. The painting amply justifies the claim that it was not 'neglected in any part'. But the question remains as to whether, and in what way, it might be thought to be more than the sum total of those parts. What is the *point* of it?

That this is a genuinely elusive issue is shown by the diversity of interpretative comment that the work has elicited.[5] It has been seen, for example, as an allegory of the Ages of Man, or as a personal work in which Constable himself, as the farmer by the gate, is 'contemplating his own past' in the shape of the drinking boy. A more recent commentator has argued that Constable deliberately filled his picture with agricultural improbabilities and anomalies in order to create 'an illusory countryside'. But this view has been vigorously rebutted, and the counter-claim advanced that Constable in fact 'went to extraordinary lengths to reach the level of realism he wished to achieve'.

This oddly wide-ranging argument comes about because the changes of title suggest absence of an extrinsic controlling 'idea' and the picture itself fails to impose an intrinsic one. It simply isn't clear how we should read the work. If it were *entitled* 'The Ages of Man' the boy, the harvesters and the church, thematically linked, would become the visual axis of the picture. Various of the natural features, such as the maimed tree, the golden corn and the shifting clouds, would take on a specific relevance to this presiding idea, as contributing allusions to evanescence, ripeness, decay. On the other hand certain elements would correspondingly dwindle in importance, subsiding into supplementary material, outside the organizing theme. Arguably the schematic reading proposed by this title would miss much of the life of the painting: the 'message' could be a lot smaller than the picture. For the same reason Claude Lorrain might well have feared that the viewer intent on the story of Jacob and Laban would fail to do justice to the landscape in which he placed them. As with the White Knight's song, what the picture is *called* isn't necessarily what it *is*.

Andrew Graham-Dixon makes a related point about another of Constable's paintings, *The Leaping Horse:* 'he has, apparently, *left out the subject*'.[6] He argues that this work, 'with its writhing trees and stormy sky', conveys a sense of drama which would seem appropriate to some great human tragedy, 'a martyrdom or crucifixion'. Given the absence of such a theme, what is the focus of all the turmoil? Graham-Dixon suggests that *The Leaping Horse*, 'like so many of Constable's mature works … is built around a composition that opposes a dense foreground of dark, wet or rotten forms to a distant, Arcadian prospect of calm and sunlit meadows'. He goes on to claim that the picture is expressive of an inner drama, the painter's ultimately unrealizable desire to recapture the happiness of his early years in the Suffolk countryside: 'It is a picture of physical struggle … that becomes an analogue for the painter's own imaginative struggle: to get from one *time* to another, from tainted adulthood to innocent childhood'.

Whatever the merits of the particular interpretation here proposed, Graham-Dixon is illustrating a further way in which a landscape painting can be felt to convey a 'meaning'. There need be no narrative, no imposed theme; an informing drama, of an imaginative or psychological kind, can be inferred from the picture as a whole, a drama expressive of conflicts within the artist's own mind. Constable has devised 'a pictorial language rich in metaphors for feeling'. That language can be left to speak for itself and to demand interpretation on its own terms.

The issues sketched above are relevant to Hardy in that he was that rare thing a landscape novelist. Repeatedly he went to great lengths to establish a particular natural environment – woodlands, a heath, the coast of north Cornwall, the rock of Portland Bill. Within that environment he would find strongly defined features to use as background – a cliff-top, a railway-cutting, a cave, a tower, a ridge of pebbles, a hollow amid the ferns.

To an extraordinary extent the action of a Hardy novel takes place out of doors. His lovers often meet for the first time in the open air – as, for example, in the cases of Tess and Angel, Oak and Bathsheba, Troy and Bathsheba, Clym and Eustacia, Pierston and Marcia, Cytherea and Springrove. Even when a character is seen indoors he or she is often being viewed not only by the reader but by another character peering in from the outdoor perspective. It is in such circumstances Dick Dewy first sets eyes on Fancy, Oak peers at Bathsheba, Bathsheba peers at Oak, de Stancy spies on Paula Power and Percomb sizes up Marty South's hair. In these cases the character indoors, almost invariably seen alone, can almost seem to be artificially isolated, shut away from the processes of normal living. The external environment regularly forces itself, in a variety of ways and at a variety of speeds, on the attention on those within. Tendrils can push through apertures, wind rattle the doors, rain dash against the panes, moths fly in at open windows. The characters are inescapably attuned to what is going on outside. Enclosed in various woodland dwellings Mrs Charmond listens to the scrape of snails against the glass, Grace looks at the small animals perambulating outside, Fitzpiers watches as passers-by negotiate a newly painted gate, and John South becomes fatally obsessed with what he sees as a threatening elm tree.

A host of activities which in most novels form part of an indoor social life are shifted to the open air by Hardy. Assignations, parties, dances, entertainments, lectures, folk-rituals can all take place out of doors. It is natural to remember many of his novels as a sequence of pictures of figures in a landscape. Habitually, and especially at the start of a narrative, he introduces the solitary pedestrian, characteristically a 'speck' on a long white road. Agricultural workers are seen toiling alone on a hillside, a field, a stretch of heath. We see Tess milking a cow, hacking swedes or feeding a threshing-machine, and Giles Winterborne planting pine trees or shrouding an elm. There are numerous outdoor pictures of a more dramatic kind: revellers dancing in the lurid light cast by a bonfire, Knight hanging from a cliff, Fanny being dragged through the night by a dog, Wildeve and Venn gambling by the light of glow-worms.

Individually and collectively such scenes pose the same questions as the landscapes of Constable and Claude. The relationship between figures and landscape is ambiguous or problematic in similar ways. The setting may function variously as neutral background, emotional echo-chamber or metaphorical commentary. More than that: it could ultimately be subject-matter in its own right. The titles of Hardy's novels suggest the potential fluctuation of focus. *Tess, Jude, The Mayor of Casterbridge*: all these point to the primacy of some particular individual. *Under the Greenwood Tree, Far from the Madding Crowd,* and *The Woodlanders* are titles which might seem to locate the essential interest in a community or an environment rather than in the doings of a human protagonist.

A particular scene is just as likely to be open to a plurality of readings. If the dice-playing of Wildeve and Venn was translated into a painting the title of the work might be variously 'Night-creatures', 'Nocturne', 'The Gamblers', 'The Intruders' or 'The Final Throw'. The doings of the men could be seen as the focus of interest, as an integral part of the total scene or as an alien intrusion. Each title would imply a different answer to the same presiding question: what has this human drama to do with the natural context?

Hardy is a landscape novelist in that he will offer a long series of such animated pictures for contemplation and suggest a stereoscopic relationship between them. Story isn't to be read in isolation from context. John Bayley goes so far as to claim that, in Hardy, 'the plot is not associated with meaning'.[7] The remark is put in perspective by a later comment: 'The small things are more important in Hardy than the big things, but in so being they also become the big things.' This is wisely said. The observation is relevant to all Hardy's descriptions, but particularly to those of nature. Figures and landscape are mutually exploratory, mutually explanatory. The reader is invited to infer a view, derived from descriptive detail scattered along the whole length of the narrative, concerning Man's place in the total scheme of things.

The Graham-Dixon reading of the two versions of *The Leaping Horse* is attractive because it begins as a response to the work as a whole, not to some detachable theme or story. Both study and finished painting are alive and expressive in every part. They *demand* a holistic response. Trees, clouds, water, animals, men, rotting stumps seem all manifestly to contribute to the artist's message. Here, too, through inherent significance and through interrelationship, the small things become the big things. It will be the central argument of this book that Hardy's fiction should be read in the same spirit. In his case, as in that of the paintings under discussion, the holistic reading incorporates alternative interpretations rather than discounting them. The story may still be enjoyed, the characters analysed; various aspects of the given work may still be seen as inherently symbolic or suggestive; but primacy should be given to the unifying vision that sponsors, energizes and incorporates all these modes of expression.

The unifying vision that I will be arguing for is not of the psychological kind that Graham-Dixon proposes in relation to *The Leaping Horse*. The drama in the agitated landscapes of Constable and Hardy may, after all, be straightforwardly attributed to nature at large. Wind, waters, plants and animals are caught up in a mutually dependent, but often fiercely antagonistic, life of their own. Why should not such conflict constitute 'subject' enough for the artist? Passage after famous passage of landscape description in Hardy's novels is alive with just this kind of movement and excitement. As a disciple of Darwin he can surely derive 'meaning' from such struggles – perhaps a significance as great as that of the human story to which the description seems, on a casual reading, to be subordinated.

Claude Lorrain's search for 'suitable' landscape subjects implies a belief that 'Nature' should feature in painting only as an amplification of some human drama. In *The Leaping Horse*, as in many of Constable's pictures, that approach is turned on its head. The human figures rather seem aspects of the wider energies in the landscape. While he was at work on his canvas Constable included in a letter a wonderfully indiscriminate account of the project:

> it is Canal. and full of the Bustle incident to such a scene where four or five boats are passing in Company with dogs. Horses boys & Men & Women & Children. and best of all old timber-props, Water plants. Willow stumps, sedges old nets &c &c &c[8]

There seems to be no assumption that the human beings mentioned are more important contributors to the 'Bustle' than the dogs or even the timber-props. In the finished picture horse and horseman strain together. The bargemen work as the moorhen flies, the water flows, the clouds swirl and the trees rock in the wind. Human energies are seen as an extension of nature's energies. The picture as a whole *includes* the ostensible subject, the leaping horse, but involves it in a huge scheme of cross-relationship between diverse entities – trees, clouds, water, wind, light, shadow, birds, cattle …

By extension the artist himself becomes part of this total complex. The passion with which he responds to the scene and sets himself to record it is all of a piece with the natural energies he portrays. His painting doesn't merely record them: it partakes of them. The wind blows, the horse leaps, the painter paints …

II

To tell a story in anything like the traditional novelistic mode is to be led, perhaps involuntarily, towards description. In the interests of definition or verisimilitude or imaginative fullness the bare facts are amplified. The nouns acquire adjectives, the verbs adverbs. The essential action is thickened out with corroborative detail. What might, for example, have been the single sentence 'John left for the office at nine' can become descriptively dilated in this sort of way:

> Gulping down a last mouthful of coffee John hurried into the hall. There wasn't even time to clean his teeth. He pulled on his black

shoes, still damp from last night's walk, and ran a comb through his thinning hair. On the door-mat was a letter which he thrust hastily into a pocket. It was cold outside, and there was a hint of rain in the air. His battered Mini started reluctantly at the third or fourth attempt. As he accelerated down the empty high street the church clock struck nine.

If this passage appeared early in a novel the ancillary detail would seem to be expository. The character is being introduced as his actions are described. But amplification of this sort is found everywhere in fiction, long after characters and context have been sufficiently established. Indeed 'amplification' is probably the wrong word, as seeming to imply that within the given novel is a detachable undecorated plot, around which the author thickens out the story by the verbal equivalent of papier mâché. In most cases, surely, the descriptive detail is intrinsic to the very conception of the work: it's not an addition to the narrative but an aspect of it, somehow part of the point.

From paragraph to paragraph the novelist, whether by instinct or design, takes scores of small decisions about the nature and scope of such material. The immediate effect may be to lend life and substance to a particular scene, but there are also longer-term implications. Cumulatively these decisions not only shape and colour the surface of the work, but suggest what aspects of daily life the writer considers to be relevant to the story being told. Inescapably they become part of the meaning of that story: they suggest that it is about these things and not about those. The author may or may not seem to be in full control of the process. Crusoe's island is described very effectively up to a point, but solely in terms of what Crusoe can turn to practical account. As a consequence it remains unvisualizable, reduced, in effect, to a combination of larder and tool-chest. In an obvious sense this is entirely reasonable: Defoe is choosing to put the emphasis on survival and self-help. The negative corollary is that his hero emerges as monomaniacally practical, betraying only spasmodic emotional responses and no aesthetic ones. In *New Grub Street* Gissing is very informative about food, clothes and lodgings at, and just above, subsistence level. His characters, like Crusoe, are struggling to survive. But as writers or artists, at least in hope and intention, they do have an aesthetic life despite their economic tribulations. It's therefore relevant for Gissing to describe a statue or a landscape: such things are very much within his characters' field of experience. Reardon will stand in leaking boots watching a beautiful sunset. Boots and sunset are equally parts of his story. If, over the length of the novel, the boots seem to predominate, that emphasis is true to the experiences being related. Reardon's poverty eventually maims his finer sensibilities.

In both these cases, however, it could be argued that the descriptive habit is more limiting and more revealing than the writer intends. It can't plausibly be claimed that *Robinson Crusoe* shows Defoe tailoring his method to the plight of a castaway; in his other novels there tends to be the same absence of visual life, the same stress on survival and possessions. His heroes and even his heroines show a Crusoe-like mentality, an unnerving materialism and solipsism which would seem, given the absence of alternative perspectives, to be shared by Defoe himself. The mode of seeing that he displays across the range of his fiction is unwittingly an exercise in self-portraiture. Gissing, similarly, shows a *general* tendency to describe the world from the point of view of a dyspeptic aesthete.

The point is worth expanding. Save in a few exceptional instances (notably the Portsmouth section of *Mansfield Park*) Jane Austen has little to say on food, clothes, creature comforts, work or the beauties of nature. Such features of life would seem to lie outside the pattern of interests within which her characters must make their decisions about love and conduct. The arena thus negatively outlined could be seen, according to taste, as bracingly uncluttered or prejudicially restricted.

These examples need not be further argued here. They are quoted only to support two general contentions central to the argument of this book – that the contingent life in a work of fiction is likely to contribute significantly to its meaning and effect, whether positively or by negation, and that it can do so in ways that the author may not fully have anticipated.

The reader's reaction to these descriptive elements will depend on their apparent relevance and usefulness. Such a passage as the invented one featured above is provisional in its initial effect, posing a variety of possible questions that the unfolding story may answer. These may be merely functional: Will the unread letter prove important? Why is the protagonist in such a hurry? Will his car break down? If the text in question were a whodunnit the reader would be looking hard at material of this sort for possible concealed clues concerning murder and murderer. A more ambitious work might seem to propose relevance of an abstract kind. In *Daniel Deronda* George Eliot follows a dense description of a station waiting-room with the comment:

Contemptible details these, to make part of a history; yet the turn of most lives is hardly to be accounted for without them. They are continually entering with cumulative force into a mood until it gets the mass and momentum of a theory or a motive. (Chapter XXI)

Obviously it is possible, not to say desirable, that any given detail may be vivid in itself, may prove to have some specific functional useful-ness, yet may also ultimately contribute, in the way Eliot suggests, to a variety of conceptual patterns. Here, having vividly evoked the dreari-ness of Gwendolen Harleth's return home, she uses the description to show us how Gwendolen's beliefs and conduct (and by inference our own) are imperceptibly modified, over a period of time, by small diurnal material circumstances. On this view a faithful account of Gwendolen's downfall must *necessarily* stoop to 'dirty paint' and dusty decanters.

Such 'things' are close to the heart of my topic. Few poets have shown more than a spasmodic and highly selective interest in them, and the dramatist remits responsibility in this area to the director or designer. By contrast novelists from Defoe onwards have engaged with clutter. Fiction is full of objects. On the one hand there are those made by man – pencils, pocket-knives, handkerchiefs, gloves, boots, ciga-rettes, spectacles, clocks, crockery, tables, cupboards, wheelbarrows, bee-hives, streetlamps, railings, walls, fences ... On the other hand there are the phenomena of nature – rocks, fossils, plants, rainbows, icicles. Objects of either kind can play a significant role in fiction as embody-ing an element of truth. An umbrella, a cheese sandwich, a sheep or a stile is an accepted unit of currency transferable between life and art. The novel that features such things can gain in definition and reso-nance through seeming to be shaped around familiar reference-points and determinants. More generally, one of the glories of the genre has been its generous willingness to engage with workaday materials of just this kind, to make them part of the artistic enterprise, to find meanings in the stuff of everyday life.

It must be admitted that these aspects of fiction are particularly hard to appreciate and assess. At first glance the game may seem an easy one to play: many a third-rate novelist distends his text with casual accounts of clothes or streets or cloudy skies. The truth is, of course, that it's an easy game to play *badly*. But even in the case of a writer whose descriptive powers noone would take lightly – a Tolstoy or an Eliot – many of the descriptive passages are likely, almost by definition, to seem incidental and miscellaneous in the first instance, and to be distributed elusively along the whole length of the novel concerned. More grandiose entities – a character, a theme, a moral, a metaphorical pattern – can readily be isolated for analysis and admiration: how is one to assemble and appraise these scattered bits and pieces?

III

The question has particular relevance to Hardy's fiction, for here is a writer instinctively drawn to physical detail. Quite often this descriptive intensity precipitates in lists:

> In the corner stood the sheep-crook, and along a shelf at one side were ranged bottles and canisters of the simple preparations pertaining to ovine surgery and physic – spirits of wine, turpentine, tar, magnesia, ginger, and castor oil being the chief. On a triangular shelf across the corner stood bread, bacon, cheese, and a cup for ale or cider, which was supplied from a flagon beneath. (*FMC*, 17)

> The agricultural and pastoral character of the people upon whom the town depended for its existence was shown by the class of objects displayed in the shop windows. Scythes, reap-hooks, sheep-shears, bill-hooks, spades, mattocks, and hoes, at the ironmonger's: bee-hives, butter-firkins, churns, milking-stools and pails, hay-rakes, field-flagons, and seed-lips, at the cooper's: cart-ropes and plough-harness at the saddler's ... (*MC*, 31)

> ... he was loading his wares – wooden bowls, dishes, spigots, spoons, cheese-vats, funnels and so on – upon one of her father's wagons ... (*Wood*, 159)

The seriousness of Hardy's interest in such tools and chattels is shown in a letter he sent to his publisher prior to the serialization of *Far from the Madding Crowd*:

> In reference to the illustrations, I have sketched in my note-book during the past summer a few correct outlines of smockfrocks, gaiters, sheep-crooks, rick-'staddles', a sheep-washing pool, one of the old-fashioned malt-houses, and some other out-of-the-way things that might have to be shown. These I could send you if they would be of any use to the artist ... (*Life*, 99)

This offer, made at the start of his career, confirms Hardy's claim, in the General Preface to the Wessex Edition of 1912, that he had been concerned 'to preserve for my own satisfaction a fairly true record of a vanishing life'. A strong component of his interest in 'stuff' is surely this desire to 'memorialise'.

This emphasis separates his descriptive habits from those of Dickens. Repeatedly a Dickensian description will serve to individualize. Many of his characters are defined by their clothes or accoutrements, houses or furnishings. Hardy sometimes works in this way. Fancy Day's boot, Anne Garland's cap-ribbons or Boldwood's locked closet reveal something of the owner's personality. But there is a necessary limit to what Hardy can do in this line, since he was portraying, even for his contemporaries, an unfamiliar world. There would have been little point in making Gabriel Oak's hut or Tess's working-clothes atypical since the reader could have had little sense of the norms from which they diverged. Hardy's interest in furnishings and farm-implements is similarly generic in emphasis, suggesting: 'this is how clothes were stored', 'this is how a mattress was made', 'this is how a sheep was sheared'.

At this level of housing, clothes, tools, accoutrements, what is conveyed above all is the sense of an established mode of life – of a community working and socializing in certain ways. 'The Dorsetshire Labourer' begins with a forceful argument against stereotyping the agricultural worker, but as the essay proceeds Hardy is happy to generalize – as, for example, in describing the loading of the waggon when a family moves house:

> The goods are built up on the waggon to a well-nigh unvarying pattern, which is probably as peculiar to the country labourer as the hexagon to the bee. The dresser, with its finger-marks and domestic evidences thick upon it, stands importantly in front, over the backs of the shaft horses, in its erect and natural position, like some Ark of the Covenant, which must not be handled slightingly or overturned. The hive of bees is slung up to the axle of the waggon, and alongside it the cooking pot or crock, within which are stowed the roots of garden flowers. (*Personal Writings*, 178)

The description is sociological, almost ethnological, in character. People in the communities concerned are shown to have in common certain patterns of householdry, conduct and custom. The fact that Hardy could borrow extracts from 'The Dorsetshire Labourer' for insertion into his novels suggests how literal his fiction is likely to be in its workaday aspects.[9]

Surprisingly, however, Hardy does *not* appear to attempt a rounded and coherent depiction of the rural life which he documents. His communities are curiously fragmented, the households widely scattered. In none of his novels is there a village imaginable in detail, with streets, shops, a church, a school, an inn. Fancy Day is a teacher in name only: we do not see her in front of a class. Dick doesn't, as might have been expected, contrive to meet her by collecting his younger siblings from school – in fact they fade out of the narrative altogether. Neither the Dewy household, in its day-to-day aspect, nor the village, as such, is invested with full imaginative life. Weatherbury, Overcombe, Marlott, Marygreen and Little Hintock are similarly elusive. Henchard's Casterbridge is the exceptional case, a full-scale depiction, topographical and social, of the life of a whole town.

There is a paradox, perhaps even a contradiction, hereabouts. For all Hardy's eagerness to evoke a bygone way of life where the sense of community was strong, his leading characters are usually solitaries. Bathsheba, Boldwood, Oak, Troy, Henchard, Susan, Giles Winterbourne, Jude Fawley, Sue Bridehead can hardly muster a couple of close relatives between them. Close friends are as rare. Who could Anne Garland or Marty South or Grace Melbury or Clym Yeobright confide in? In *Jude,* Gillingham does feature specifically in the role of friend, but having no individual life or personality, he seems to have been wheeled on solely to provide occasion for the miserable Phillotson to articulate his reflections on marriage.

There *is* some cheerful social life in Hardy – for example, the parties in *Under the Greenwood Tree, The Trumpet-Major,* and *The Return of the Native* – but most of his characters are far from being naturally gregarious. George Eliot's protagonists predominantly, Austen's almost exclusively, inhabit a social medium; Hardy's do not. The party which Giles holds for Grace is something of a disaster, but given the paucity of tolerable guests in the vicinity a social triumph can never have been on the cards. The success of Farfrae's fair, in *The Mayor of Casterbridge,* is balanced by the failure of Henchard's. One can't readily conceive of Elizabeth-Jane Henchard, Diggory Venn or Jude Fawley having a few friends round for the evening.

It comes about, therefore, that all sorts of descriptive opportunities which Dickens would have exploited to the full Hardy chooses to disregard. He says relatively little about domestic interiors, seeming as little interested in the topography of a house or cottage as in the topography of a village. He says little about neighbours, personal possessions, meals, shopping, leisure activities, domestic doings, indoor life in general.

Yet it is the very solitariness of his wandering characters which provides the occasions for much of Hardy's description. He alternately observes them and looks through their eyes as they walk and watch and reflect and interpret. What they perceive will be predominantly the phenomena of nature: hills, rivers, trees, animals, birds, clouds, stars, sunsets, weather. Set against these powers is a scattering of man-made objects: buildings, roads, walls, fences. Through the progress of a whole narrative recurrent allusions to such scenery agglomerate into a powerful evocation of context, a landscape context. As in a landscape painting it provides not only a physical but a conceptual background.

Many of Hardy's characters, however, have a special status which makes them more than neutral 'figures' adrift in the landscape. As agricultural workers they know how to glean practical information from what they see. They can read tracks, forecast the weather, tell the time by the stars. Nature is shown to be rich in 'meanings', of which these are only the most immediately practical examples. Hardy teaches and encourages other modes of 'reading'. His landscapes everywhere offer tacit commentary on the changeability and brevity of life, on conflict and mutual dependence, on destruction and adaptation, on the instinct to survive and procreate, on the processes of ageing and erosion. One inference is that folk who can read nature's simpler messages – and even some who can't – may in some sense apprehend these darker ones. Such characters are repeatedly portrayed as assimilating what they see and hear into their private dramas. The external sights and sounds may influence the inner life, as when the flatness of Egdon Heath magnifies Eustacia's frustrations. Alternatively the private drama may colour what is seen, as when the pregnant Tess reads reproach into an impassive landscape. In either case the tacit suggestion is that human beings instinctively cross-relate their personal lives and the life of nature at large, interpreting each in the light of the other. It is a claim that readers unwittingly and inescapably endorse if they are beguiled into accepting that the human story Hardy is telling and the natural context he is describing are so closely affined that the former would be incomplete without ample reference to the latter.

IV

It might be as well, at this point, to consider some of the ways in which which Hardy's 'backgrounds' have been discussed in the past. There has been prolific praise for them, but it can easily, and understandably, subside into platitude, especially in relation to the big set-piece descriptions: 'The human drama is enacted against the timeless backdrop of the heath / the woods / the sea-cliffs …'. The tendency has often been to make Hardy's landscapes seem no more than inert settings, something like the scenery for a play. The position is a familiar one, and scarcely calls for elaboration.

It has also long been recognized, however, that much of the descriptive detail should be read metaphorically. In certain cases Hardy's experiments in this kind are assertively self-explanatory. Few readers will miss the point of the flying pizzle in *Jude*, or of the maimed trees in *The Woodlanders*, or of the Stonehenge scene in *Tess*. As early as *Far from the Madding Crowd* Hardy famously devotes several paragraphs to investing Bathsheba's ancient barn with symbolic status. Less obviously he is already, in that novel, beginning to attach a habitual metaphorical significance to what might seem incidental features of a scene, such as windows, gates and doorways.[10]

But these might be considered special cases. What, if anything, is to be said of the routine scene-painting, neither dramatic backdrop nor metaphorical comment, which seems to fulfil no specialized local purpose? Here is an example from *The Mayor of Casterbridge*:

> Next morning, accordingly, she rose at five o'clock, and went into the street. It was not yet light; a dense fog prevailed, and the town was as silent as it was dark, except that from the rectangular avenues which framed in the borough there came a chorus of tiny rappings, caused by the fall of water-drops condensed on the boughs; now it was wafted from the West Walk, now from the South Walk; and then from both quarters simultaneously. (239)

It is a delicate and attractive passage, but it has no obvious immediate function. The episode which it introduces consists of a brief dialogue between Elizabeth-Jane and Farfrae, concluded within a single page. Neither the state of the weather nor the atmosphere of the streets is relevant to what passes between them. In terms of the narrative the chapter could as well have begun 'Next morning Elizabeth-Jane was at Farfrae's door soon after five'.

Hardy's fiction is, of course, full of descriptive passages of this apparently incidental kind. Is it to be assumed that they are merely decorative additions, picturesque but dispensable, superior versions of the gestures towards local colour which a hack storyteller might make? If they amount to more than that, how and why do they do so? What, if anything, do they convey, or contribute to?

In one sense the *Mayor of Casterbridge* passage might be seen as an exceptional case, since, as suggested earlier, this is the one novel in

which Hardy assembles a comprehensive account of a social and working environment. We are shown Casterbridge from a wide variety of
aspects. The quoted paragraph is one detail among many contributing
to the total picture: here is Casterbridge at waking time. A later sentence depicts the change as the town comes more fully to life: 'Thus
they parted, and she went homeward, journeymen now being in the
street, waggoners going to the harness-maker's for articles left to be
repaired, farm-horses going to the shoeing smiths, and the sons of
labour showing themselves generally on the move' (240).

   But of course there are many comparably 'dispensable' passages in
the other novels, where no such overall picture is being sketched.
What do they convey? To start with, a sense that it is simply Hardy's
imaginative habit to tell his stories in these terms: the description
emerges naturally with the narration. He would seem to assume that
this is how people – at least how quite a number of people – respond to
daily life. They think, feel and see at the same time, and the experiences become one. Elizabeth-Jane's absorption in her purpose doesn't
preclude a consciousness of her surroundings. It may even be that in
her anxious mood she notices them more sharply, picking up the 'tiny
rappings' of the water-drops because she is alert for the sound of
Farfrae's front door and of his footsteps. The description may indirectly
convey a quickened state of apprehension.

   It is because the mood of Hardy's characters is so often compounded,
in this way, with what they see and hear, that a larger metaphorical
strategy is open to him – one that took an appreciable time to win critical recognition. Emotional or psychological states may be displaced
altogether into the landscape. The morning after receiving Bathsheba's
Valentine Boldwood rises early. He goes outside and, at what has
become a turning-point in his life, gazes at a strange wintry landscape.
Fields and sky are so similar in colour that it is hard to locate a horizon
line. Because of the snow there is the 'preternatural inversion of light
and shade which attends the prospect when the garish brightness com-
monly in the sky is found on the earth and the shades of the earth are
in the sky' (104). The bleak sunrise resembles a sunset 'as childhood
resembles age'. In the west lingers 'the wasting moon, now dull and
greenish yellow, like tarnished brass'. At the literal level this strong
description richly evokes the mood of a bleak February day. But the
unfamiliarity, the ominousness, the sense of disorientation, as in a world
turned upside-down – all this is primarily an account of Boldwood's
uncertain and uneasy state of mind. More is hinted of his mood, of
his hopes and fears, than could well have been expressed by internal

monologue. As in two parallel daybreak scenes in the novel – which follow, respectively, the loss of Oak's sheep and the opening of Fanny's coffin – the mental landscape is more important than the physical one.

This mode of expression is exploited by Hardy to considerable effect. It is particularly useful in the case of a Boldwood or a Giles Winterborne – characters who repress their feelings. There will be further illustrations of the method in the chapters that follow, but it has come to be widely acknowledged, and in this book will be no more than a sub-theme.

The major theme is more easy to illustrate than to summarize. A preliminary clue can be derived from Hardy's early work, because his descriptive method, like his distinctive prose-style, was fully in evidence from the start of his fictional career. In fact its assured complexity can conveniently be illustrated by a comparison between extracts from his first two novels about country life. The chosen passages both appear early in the work concerned, at a point where the writer's freedom of descriptive manoeuvre is not yet constrained by narrative responsibilities. The first is the very beginning of *Under the Greenwood Tree*. Even within this opening paragraph the voice and the preoccupations are immediately recognizable as Hardy's – indeed his authorship declares itself in the first five words:

> To dwellers in a wood, almost every species of tree has its voice as well as its feature. At the passing of the breeze the fir-trees sob and moan no less distinctly than they rock: the holly whistles as it battles with itself: the ash hisses amid its quivering: the beech rustles while its flat boughs rise and fall. And winter, which modifies the note of such trees as shed their leaves, does not destroy its individuality. (11)

This is one in a long line of Hardy night-scenes. The darkness, so far from inhibiting description, makes it more scrupulously attentive. The fascination with trees is to prove typical: in this case birch and elm will be added to the list within a couple of paragraphs. Each of the barely seen species is recognizable, at any rate to 'dwellers in a wood', through movement – 'rock', 'quivering', 'rise and fall' – and through sound. Both characteristics are noticeable because, as so often in Hardy's descriptions, a wind is blowing. The 'individuality' of the trees involves an element of personification; the claimed 'voice' sounds almost human as it sobs, moans, whistles or hisses.

Further movement and sound are supplied by Dick Dewy, who walks briskly along the lane singing a folk-song. He is to be the hero of the novel, but in the darkness he at first has no more individuality than the trees. Even when he emerges into view it is only as a silhouetted figure with 'an ordinary-shaped nose, an ordinary chin, an ordinary neck and ordinary shoulders'. Human status is given a timely boost when his friends appear, also in silhouette, looking like 'some processional design on Greek or Etruscan pottery'. After all, these 'ordinary' men belong to an ancient tradition of country living, dignified in art for many centuries. Nonetheless the prevailing message of this opening section is to do not merely with the harmony but with the affinities between man, trees, wind and stars.

Far from the Madding Crowd opens with a description of Gabriel Oak which is clumsy, if not downright belittling. It begins from his comical Dickensian smile (which is rarely to irradiate the ensuing narrative) and places emphasis on his clothes – especially his large, impermeable boots – and his huge, useless, Captain Cuttle watch. He is said to be 'of sound judgment...and general good character'. His physical appearance, even by daylight, would seem to rival Dick Dewy's nocturnal silhouette for comprehensive ordinariness: 'not a single lineament could be selected and called worthy either of distinction or notoriety' (11).

The second chapter of the novel, however, gives a much fuller and more impressive view of Oak, partly by showing him at work, partly by associating him with the landscape in which that work is carried out. The opening paragraphs of the chapter are very close, in spirit and in detail, to the opening paragraphs of *Under the Greenwood Tree*. Again this is a night-scene at a lonely place in late December; there are stars overhead and dead leaves under foot. Again a breeze is blowing, producing a 'sob' and 'moan' of foliage. Again a solitary man makes music of his own among the noises of nature. The vocal beech-trees grow on Norcombe Hill, 'a featureless convexity of chalk and soil' which for all its commonplace aspect conveys an impressive sense of indestructibility.

It has been rightly pointed out that Oak gains in stature from his metaphorical association with this hill. His similar ordinariness, as the story is to demonstrate, masks a similar solidity. The metaphor goes further. Oak is a quiet man who rarely chooses to disclose his feelings; the varied eloquence of the vegetation on Norcombe Hill hints at own hidden emotional intensities. The trees seem to lament like human beings; they moan, sob or wail. The obverse point is made a couple of chapters later, when the proposal to Bathsheba goes wrong: 'Oak sighed a deep honest sigh – none the less so in that, being like the sigh of a pine plantation, it was rather noticeable as a disturbance of the atmosphere' (35).

Even the night sky is to tell us something about him. Readers ready to patronize him for the uselessness of his watch may feel a new respect when it transpires that he can tell the time by the stars. Nor can he be dismissed as a crude utilitarian:

> 'One o'clock,' said Gabriel.
> Being a man not without a frequent consciousness that there was some charm in this life he led, he stood still after looking at the sky as a useful instrument, and regarded it in an appreciative spirit, as a work of art superlatively beautiful. (17)

It's conceivable that the first chapter of the novel is a deliberate false start, presenting a stereotype which the author means to qualify forthwith. The Gabriel Oak initially portrayed isn't far removed from the conventional clownish 'Hodge' elsewhere disclaimed by Hardy. This second chapter rehabilitates him, suggesting a range of knowledge, skill and feeling that the first never allowed for. It does this not by direct portraiture, but by associating him with a rich and diverse natural environment, strikingly portrayed, and showing him to be at home in it, able to understand its voices and read its signs.

The two passages have in common a remarkable energy. The second sentence of *Under the Greenwood Tree*, quoted above, contains nine verbs as well as a couple of verbal nouns. A wind is blowing, the trees are threshing – even the sky is full of activity: '... the white stars twinkled so vehemently that their flickering seemed like the flapping of wings'. A similar observation is made in *Far from the Madding Crowd*: '... the twinkling of all the stars seemed to be but throbs of one body, timed by a common pulse' (14). In the later novel Hardy goes farther, and evokes the sense one can have on such a night of the whole world speeding 'through the stars'. There is movement everywhere, and Oak contributes to it as he busies himself about the field, 'the lantern light appearing and disappearing here and there, and brightening him or darkening him as he stood before or behind it' (15–16). Soon he is retrieving a new-born lamb. Elsewhere on the hill Bathsheba and her aunt are tending a day-old calf. In *Under the Greenwood Tree* the assembled Mellstock choir have a hearty meal and then go on their round amid the occasional 'bark of foxes' or 'brush of a rabbit'.

Conveyed in these sequences, in their totality, is the suggestion that the fallen leaves, the wind, the singing, swishing trees, the flickering stars, the animal life and the human life are all aspects of the same process – to the extent that the human doings are assigned no clear priority. The two passages might be thought atypical in that they involve extended set-pieces of description which are essentially preludes. An alternative view would be that this early pattern of emphasis is designed to establish a methodology for the whole succeeding narrative. In his later novels Hardy repeatedly chooses to include such a set-piece within the first couple of chapters. It tells his readers what his medium is to be; it shows them what to look out for and how to read. It reminds them that 'nature', in his fiction, is not background but subject-matter. Here in concentrated form are the descriptive habits that will characterise the text as a whole. There will be more trees, more winds, more sounds, more darkness, more stars, more animal life, more movement. The cross-relationships made manifest in the set-pieces will operate between the numerous briefer passages of description to come. The life that infuses these introductory descriptions will infuse the narrative as a whole, implying a fuller 'subject' than that supplied by the human drama.

V

The note on the landscape-painting of Claude and Constable should have been sufficient, brief as it was, to suggest the difficulties they faced in reconciling the oppositions implicit in their chosen genre: narrative and background, statement and meditation, stasis and motion, the human and the non-human. Hardy, through a conflict of personal habits of response, was compelled to grapple with much the same tensions. A characteristically diverse passage in the *Life* encapsulates the problem:

"Rowed on the Stour in the evening, the sun setting up the river. Just afterwards a faint exhalation visible on surface of water as we stirred it with the oars. A fishy smell from the numerous eels and other fish beneath. Mowers salute us. Rowed among the water-lilies to gather them. Their long ropy stems.

"Passing the island drove out a flock of swallows from the bushes and sedge, which had gone there to roost. Gathered meadow-sweet. Rowed with difficulty through the weeds, the rushes on the border standing like palisades against the bright sky ... A Cloud in the sky like a huge quill-pen."

Another entry at this time:

"A story has been told me of a doctor at Maiden Newton, who attended a woman who could not pay him. He said he would take the dead baby in payment. He had it, and it was kept on his mantel-piece in a large glass jar in spirits, which stained the body brown. The doctor, who was a young man, afterwards married and used his wife badly, insisting on keeping the other woman's dead baby on his mantelpiece." (115)

The *Life* is, among other things, an intriguing anthology of the memoranda, descriptive and anecdotal, that Hardy thought worth preserving. These particular jottings date from the summer of 1876, when he and Emma had just moved into 'their first house', at Sturminster Newton. Both are instantly recognizable as Hardy's work. The account of the evening's boating is characteristically full of sensuous life and movement: mowers in the fields, fish in the river, swallows in the air; the sun sinks, an 'exhalation' rises, the boat struggles through weeds, rushes and flowers. There is material for descriptive poetry here; indeed the passage harks forward to 'Overlooking the River Stour' or 'On Sturminster Foot-Bridge'.

The entry that follows is equally typical of its author, in this case for its macabre black humour and its potentiality for both tragedy and farce. Hardy could well have written it up as a 'sensational' short story, similar in flavour to 'The Withered Arm'; but then again the doctor concerned is not unlike a major figure in one of his novels – the Fitzpiers who purchases human brains.

Although the passages are juxtaposed they seem to point in very different directions. The black anecdote is pure narrative, self-contained, seemingly resistant to descriptive embellishment of any kind. Conversely the account of the boat-trip has nothing to say about those centrally concerned – presumably Thomas and Emma Hardy – but leads away from them. The observing writer is lost in what he sees; hence the drift from past tense to present tense, and the unexpected similes that give a further edge of visual definition. To put the case diagrammatically, the story illustrates Hardy's narrative impulse and the descriptive passage his poetic impulse. How were the two modes be cross-related? How was Hardy the teller of unadorned tales to find house-room for the Hardy who mused on meadow-sweet, swallows and eels? How was the poetic description to be accommodated in a prose story – particularly the odd kind of prose story intriguing to this idiosyncratic observer?

Hardy was in some senses a narrow writer. It has been noted that he repeatedly rings the changes on the same basic tale. A girl – Fancy Day, Bathsheba, Elfride, Eustacia, Ethelberta, Grace, Tess, Sue – must choose between two or more lovers. The situation within which the choice has to be made is elevated to melodramatic intensity and usually brings about the death of at least one of these lovers, or of the girl herself. Drama on this scale seems to have been intrinsic to Hardy's idea of a tale 'exceptional enough to justify its telling' (*Life*, 268). But he could quite feasibly squeeze such action into a short story – and in fact often did so. Many of these tales – which he calls 'minor novels' – could in summary seem to offer enough substance for a full-length work in Hardy's characteristic manner. Conversely some of the full-scale works are sparse enough, in terms of cast and plot, to be reducible to short stories. Hardy distinguishes between the genres in a number of ways, but the most obvious difference is certainly in contextual density, particularly in realization of place, and accounts of landscape, season and weather. In practice it is the descriptive energies, potentially extrinsic, which provide the defining substance of his novels. Film and television adaptations tend to fall short to the extent that they concentrate on character and story at the expense of this 'substance'.

Clearly, then, Hardy does find effective ways of fusing melodramatic narrative and natural description. Various of these methods will be explored in detail in the ensuing chapters. At this stage in the argument one or two preliminary hints might offer a helpful bearing-point.

In places the potential discrepancy of aims is mitigated by the fact that nature itself can be melodramatic in its extremer manifestations – gale, flood, drought or storm. If the story is larger than life then so, often, is the setting. A more significant mediating factor is that Hardy's essential interest, even in melodramatic and supernatural tales, lies in feeling and motive. It is the psychology behind the macabre tale that intrigues him. It has already been suggested that landscape description in Hardy has also a psychological dimension. The transition between the two journal entries quoted above is hardly more drastic than that between Chapter 43 of *Far from the Madding Crowd*, in which Bathsheba unscrews Fanny's coffin, and Chapter 44, in which she awakens under a tree at dawn, amid the sounds of birds and squirrels. The sequence in the novel seems effortless because in both chapters the main focus of interest is Bathsheba's state of mind. The coffin and its contents are not described with the grim humour of the dead-baby anecdote or the grisly relish of 'Barbara of the House of Grebe'. The comments on 'the silent ones', even in the fuller manuscript version, are delicate and compassionate. As Bathsheba weeps beside the coffin the emphasis is on her plight, on the 'complicated origin' of her tears – an origin 'of a nature indescribable, almost indefinable'. But just as the events of the night torment her 'heated fancy', so the sights and sounds of the morning serve to cool her and bring solace. The descriptive opening pages of Chapter 44 are not simply an interlude of calm for the reader, they have an immediate psychological relevance, both demonstrating and explaining the first stages in Bathsheba's recovery.

This mingling of modes, a version of Dickens's 'streaky bacon' effect,[11] is already in evidence in Hardy's first novel, *Desperate Remedies*. A relevant side-light is his admission, in the Prefatory Note of 1912, that he included in the text various cannibalized verses which, as it happened, were eventually to be published in their original form: '... as the author could not get them printed, he incontinently used here whatever of their content came into his head as being apt for the purpose – after dissolving it into prose, never anticipating at that time that the poems would see the light' (*DR*, 38). 'Incontinently' is too harsh, in seeming to suggest reckless self-plagiarism. Most of the borrowings that have been identified are incidental. Only one poem – 'She, to Him II' – is at all closely paraphrased (p. 272) and there the sentiment concerned is particularly important to Hardy: he recapitulates it again in *Tess* (96). But it is interesting to note that from the start of his novelistic career, even when trying to write a mystery-thriller in the Wilkie Collins mode, he not only felt that he could modulate between verse and prose, but categorically made occasions for including the kind of material that he would have preferred to fashion into poems. In particular the descriptive aspect of the novels is put at the disposal of Hardy the poet. His 'idiosyncrasy of regard' is equally suited to either medium. For example, a vigorous narrative paragraph in 'The Three Strangers' includes the sentence: 'At the second time of closing in they found themselves near a lonely ash, the single tree on this part of the coomb, probably sown there by a passing bird some fifty years before' (*Complete Stories*, 22). The final clause derives from Hardy's earliest poem, 'Domicilium':

> ... and from a pit
> An oak uprises, springing from a seed
> Dropped by some bird a hundred years ago.

The idea is equally comfortable in either context, equally pleasing in its sudden shift of perspective. Hardy can accommodate such observations in a story or a novel because he has devised a narrative medium that leaves a wide margin for description and reflection. The sensibility and imagination that flourish in the poems have scope to pervade the fiction.

It's not surprising, therefore, that the 'borrowing' process can operate in reverse. The novels can themselves beget poems. 'Tess's Lament' and 'The Well-Beloved' are only the most obvious examples. More generally there are numerous poems that might equally have anticipated a fictional text or derived from it, just as there are numerous passages in the novels that read like potential poems. *The Woodlanders*, for example, relates to a sizeable group of 'tree-poems' including 'The Ivy-Wife', 'In a Wood', 'The Pine Planters', 'Throwing a Tree', 'The Ageing House', 'Logs on the Hearth' and 'The Felled Elm and She'. A recurring theme in these poems, as in the novel, is the comparability and the interconnectedness between the lives of men and the lives of trees. Repeatedly, in *The Woodlanders*, Hardy incorporates just the kind of description or observation that sponsored such poems. In some episodes – for example, the dying of John South – the thematic statement derives directly from the plot itself. More frequently it grows out of some seemingly parenthetical passage of description. The characters are 'woodlanders': their doings are reflected in the natural environment and at the same time influenced by it.

> Here, as everywhere, the Unfulfilled Intention, which makes life what it is, was as obvious as it could be among the depraved crowds of a city slum. The leaf was deformed, the curve was crippled, the taper was interrupted; the lichen ate the vigour of the stalk, and the ivy slowly strangled to death the promising sapling. (41)

This well-known passage contains pretty well the whole substance of 'In a Wood' (subscribed *See 'The Woodlanders'*) and with its tautness, balance and forceful rhythms is arguably superior to the poem.

Correspondences at this level are obvious enough. It wouldn't be difficult to find further set-piece comparisons of this kind across the whole range of Hardy's poetry and fiction. But the point of this book will be rather to show that similar 'poetic' impulses are to be traced in the very grain of Hardy's descriptive passages, short or long. What in the work of many a 'traditional' novelist is merely enabling matter, casual amplification, or 'corroborative detail', can be central to his purpose. Hardy the storyteller instinctively creates opportunities for Hardy the poet, and the incorporated poetry modifies the meaning of the story he tells. To read the novels in their fullness we must read even the detail attentively: the small things 'become the big things'.

2
Hardy's Insects

Animals and birds play a significant part in Hardy's work, often encroaching not only upon the feelings and thoughts but upon the very fortunes of his characters. Henchard's love for Elizabeth-Jane is expressed by his gift of a caged goldfinch. Elfride lets her horse decide whether or not she should elope. Gabriel Oak's life is saved by one of his dogs and his livelihood destroyed by another. The Durbeyfield family is ruined by the death of their horse. It would be a simple task to write a long and diverse chapter on these interconnections. Indeed the task would be simultaneously too easy and too large. The range and scale of the issues concerned can perhaps be sufficiently implied by a discussion of the related but far more confined topic of Hardy's insects.

The fictional potentiality of insects would seem to be meagre. They do not engage our affections and save for the odd bite or sting are involved in few transactions with humankind. More than that: they are small, elusive, unnoticeable – altogether out of scale with Man. Why should a novelist bother to take account of them? At the technical level, how is a writer praised for his sharply focused portrayal of character to achieve the descriptive depth of field to record anything but the bare presence of the occasional bee or butterfly? Nonetheless insects are copiously present in Hardy's work. There is no novel by him in which an insect doesn't make a creep-on, or fly-in, appearance. In many there is repeated reference to a separate, simultaneous world of tiny creatures: flies, crane-flies, bees, wasps, moths, butterflies, ants, beetles, grasshoppers, gnats, woodlice, caterpillars, snails and slugs. No doubt Hardy acquires an extra edge of authority from the acuity of apprehension which their presence implies. 'He was a man who used to notice such things': since he proves sensitive to sights and sounds so small we are the more likely to trust his observation elsewhere. But it would need a stronger argument than this to justify the presence of so *many* insects. When, why and how does Hardy introduce them? In what ways, if any, do their miniaturized activities display the workings of his imagination?

At first glance these frequent references might seem to represent no more than an extension of his general respect and consideration for all living creatures. In 'An August Midnight', when the longlegs, the moth, the dumbledore and the fly invade Hardy's desk and 'besmear my new-penned line', he shows no impatience. 'Thus meet we five', he remarks, democratically, as he observes their conduct with a courteous, attentive eye. Such sympathy is often dramatized in the novels. In the last of them the young Jude treads carefully lest he crush an earthworm (*Jude*, 11). In one of the first, Geoffrey Day shows himself anxious to treat his bees with humanity: 'The proper way to take honey, so that the bees be neither starved nor murdered is a puzzling matter' (*UGT*, 146). He avoids the new method of fumigation because it means that 'the pangs o' death be twice upon 'em'. Even when repeatedly stung by some bees trapped in his clothing he comments with placid sympathy: '...they can't sting me many times more, poor things; for they must be getting weak' (147). By contrast it's probably an ominous sign that Sergeant Troy, in the sword-play scene, casually executes a caterpillar to show off his fencing skills (*FMC*, 195).

'An August Midnight' also implies that there might be something to be learned from insects: 'They know Earth-secrets that know not I'. Hardy's 'native' characters, who can interpret nature's hints, know that there may be hidden significance in the movements of cattle or birds. The truly adept pick up still slighter signals. Gabriel Oak recognizes omens of an impending storm in the doings of a toad, a slug and two spiders before seeking confirmation in the reactions of his sheep. Insects provide meteorological small print for those practical observers equipped to read it.

But Hardy frequently introduces them for subtler, more abstract reasons. In *Desperate Remedies*, his first novel, the idiosyncrasy is already evident. A notable example is the scene which follows Manston's proposal to Cytherea and her rejection of him. Left to himself he stares into a water-butt:

> The reflection from the smooth stagnant surface tinged his face with the greenish shades of Correggio's nudes. Staves of sunlight slanted down through the still pool, lighting it up with wonderful distinctness. Hundreds of thousands of minute living creatures sported and tumbled in its depth with every contortion that gaiety

could suggest; perfectly happy, though consisting only of a head, or a tail, or at most a head and a tail, and all doomed to die within the twenty-four hours. (244)

Technically these roisterers aren't insects, but they qualify for the purposes of this discussion. On casual reading the passage seems incidental, a descriptive interlude in a densely plotted 'sensation novel'. Further consideration suggests that a good deal more is going on. Hardy solicits an attentive response: the scene is sharply lit and carefully composed – as the reference to Correggio hints. We are shown not only the 'minute living creatures' but Manston himself contemplating them, reacting to them. He is influenced by what he sees, resolving to persist in his courtship: '"Why shouldn't I be happy through my little day too?"' But it isn't that the episode has been imposed on the text to bring about a change of mood required by the plot. At this stage in the novel the action has faded into indistinctness; the only surviving narrative impulse requires Cytherea to be drawn unwillingly towards marriage with Manston. There is no serious chance that he will abandon the chase. It seems likely that the abortive proposal scene, perfunctorily disposed of in two sentences, has itself been thrown in as an excuse for the introduction of the water-butt and its thought-provoking contents. For Hardy the interpolation has intrinsic weight. It takes on greater importance retrospectively, when we find that Manston's reactions, far from being whimsical, are all of a piece with his farewell letter, which suggests an inveterate preoccupation with the brevity of life.:

I am now about to enter on my normal condition. For people are almost always in their graves. When we survey the long race of men, it is strange and still more strange to find that they are mainly dead men, who have scarcely ever been otherwise. (407)

It is the very insignificance of the tiny swimmers that prompts Manston to speculation and shapes his mood. Shortly afterwards Cytherea herself is similarly influenced:

On the right hand the sun, resting on the horizon-line, streamed across the ground from below copper-coloured and lilac clouds, stretched out in flats beneath a sky of pale soft green. All dark objects on the earth that lay towards the sun were overspread by a purple haze, against which a swarm of wailing gnats shown forth luminously, rising upward and floating away like sparks of fire.

The stillness oppressed and reduced her to mere passivity. The only wish the humidity of the place left in her was to stand motionless. The helpless flatness of the landscape gave her, as it gives all such temperaments, a sense of bare equality with, and no superiority to, a single entity under the sky. (252)

Here, of course, the scene is fuller, and the part played by the insects is less central. Neither character nor author offers to read significance into their presence. Purely implicit is the suggestion that the evening light, the humidity, the flatness make Cytherea feel of no more account than a gnat. But as with the water-butt episode not merely the mood but the very motives of the watcher are influenced. Cytherea senses that she is drifting listlessly towards marriage. Again the incident is unnecessary to the plot: nothing comes of it directly or immediately. Yet here, too, Hardy is writing with passion and scrupulosity. The prose is intent, evocative, rhythmical. Light and colour are again vividly pictured, in this second case serving to transfigure and beautify the 'swarm of wailing gnats'.

It is a measure of Hardy's engagement with these two passages that both are re-worked in *The Return of the Native*. Several sentences from the sunset scene are repeated verbatim (208–9), here providing the context in which Clym is persuaded to fix a marriage-date with Eustacia. Again there is the echo of Keats's 'Ode to Autumn' as 'wailing gnats' dance luminously in the light of the sunset, but this time both lovers feel oppressed. The mood of the occasion, 'this overpowering of the fervid by the inanimate', is sufficiently marked and distinctive for Hardy to recall it a hundred pages later (328), when Clym returns from Susan Nunsuch's cottage to make his accusations against Eustacia.

On her ill-fated visit to her married son Mrs Yeobright pauses to watch, like Manston, 'ephemerons... in mad carousal':

some in the air, some on the hot ground and vegetation, some in the tepid and stringy water of a nearly dried pool. All the shallower ponds had decreased to a vaporous mud, amid which the maggoty shapes of innumerable obscene creatures could be indistinctly seen, heaving and wallowing with enjoyment. Being a woman not disinclined to philosophise she sometimes sat down under her umbrella to rest and to watch their happiness... (*RN*, 278)

This vignette is more complex in its effect than its predecessor in *Desperate Remedies*. The tone is equivocal. 'Enjoyment', 'happiness', even 'mad carousal', are positive terms; 'maggoty', 'obscene', 'heaving and wallowing' pull the other way. Since Mrs Yeobright is preoccupied with thoughts of Clym it is hardly fanciful to see this ambiguity as reflecting mixed impulses: hope concerning the outcome of her reconciliatory visit compounded with distaste for her son's relationship with 'a voluptuous idle woman'. What she sees both images and intensifies what she feels.

The passage proves to be part of a sequence – extending over several chapters and culminating in Mrs Yeobright's death – in which the sights and sounds of Egdon Heath are made to provide a commentary on the doings of the Yeobrights and, by extension, of human beings in general. Plants, trees and birds are all featured, but insects predominate. Mrs Yeobright follows a furzecutter who appears 'of a russet hue, not more distinguishable from the scene around him than the green caterpillar from the leaf it feeds on'. He seems to be 'of no more account in life than an insect' – 'a mere parasite of the heath' (278). Only belatedly does she realize that the man she has been seeing as thus belittled is Clym himself. In Clym's own garden she notices wasps 'rolling drunk' with the juice of the apples they have been eating, 'stupefied by its sweetness' (281). To her mind, of course, Clym has been similarly 'stupefied' by the charms of Eustacia.

Later, returning homeward, sad and weary after what she assumes has been a deliberate rebuff, she sits and watches a colony of ants, 'a never-ending and heavy-laden throng': 'To look down upon them was like observing a city street from the top of a tower' (291). A comment from Johnny Nunsuch, a little earlier, has provided a hint, if a hint is needed, as to the significance of such allusions:

'Once when I went to Throope Great Pond to catch effets I seed myself looking up at myself, and I was frightened and jumped back like anything!' (*RN*, 288)

What Hardy's characters see in the doings of insects, as in nature at large, is a reflection of their own condition.

Of all the novels *The Return of the Native* is the one in which the author makes the most frequent and the most calculated references to insects. Robert Gittings has drawn attention to the specific use made of J. G. Wood's *Insects at Home*, from which Hardy had taken notes.[1] The examples quoted above can be placed within a much fuller metaphorical context, a Modernist exercise in patterning, involving all four main characters. Even prior to Mrs Yeobright's journey Clym has been shown at work among 'creeping and winged things' (253–4) that 'seemed to enrol him in their band'. He moves among bees, 'amber-coloured butterflies' and 'emerald-green grasshoppers'. Earlier still Eustacia, 'in her winter dress' has been likened to 'the tiger-beetle which, when observed in dull situations, seems to be of the quietest neutral colour, but under a full illumination blazes with dazzling splendour' (88).

Every reader of the novel will recall the bizarre scene where Wildeve and Diggory Venn gamble by the light of glow-worms. They are reduced to this pass because 'a large death's-head moth' has flown into their lantern and extinguished it. That accident finds a later echo when Wildeve invites Eustacia to an assignation by means of a moth. He slips it into the partly-open window and it blunders into the candle flame. She immediately recognizes the signal that he had used for the same purpose in the old days at Mistover.

Later, when Clym returns to Blooms-End, after his mother's death, he finds that 'a spider had already constructed a large web tying the door to the lintel, on the supposition that it was never to be opened again' (321). The abandoned house intensifies his sense of desolation. '"My life creeps like a snail"', he tells Diggory Venn (323). Everywhere the characters go their doings are somehow entangled with those of 'an unseen insect world' (291).

As the previous chapter noted, it has become a critical commonplace to see Hardy's descriptions of nature, in general, as providing figurative suggestion of various kinds. The simplest recurring metaphorical inference is that Man, in his littleness and helplessness, is akin to an animal, a bird, a tree – or an insect. In this vein Hardy describes Tess and Marian, at work in the swede-field, as 'crawling ... like flies' (277), or compares a busy highway to 'an ant-walk' (*T-M*, 101) or sees soldiers at work as 'busying themselves like cheese-mites' (*Dynasts*, 290). The teeming presence in the novels of insects, creatures so small, so ubiquitously numerous, is a continual reminder that each of us is 'one of a long row only'. The astronomer Swithin St. Cleeve feels himself 'annihilated' by his nightly study of 'monsters of magnitude' (*TT*, 33). The violent shifts of perspective to which he subjects himself are, of course, only an extremer version of those experienced by many a character in the fiction of Hardy, whose heroes and heroines regularly wield telescopes. It would come as no great surprise to hear of a lost Hardy novel which featured a scientist demoralized by regular use of the microscope to investigate 'monsters of minitude' – indeed Fitzpiers is such a character in embryo. Equally with the dizzyingly large the dizzyingly small can dramatize an impartial relativity in the universe, unflattering to Man's pretensions.

In *The Life* Hardy offers an interesting variation on this idea, in terms of a piquant inversion. He is quoting a journal entry:

'28 Nov. I sit under a tree, and feel alone: I think of certain insects around me as magnified by the microscope: creatures like elephants, flying dragons, etc. And I feel I am by no means alone.' (*Life*, 110)

Again the sense is equivocal. If 'lonely' were substituted, in both sentences, for 'alone', the emphasis would be curiously companionable – 'curiously' in that most of us would prefer a spell of loneliness to an encounter with an elephant-sized bug. The point isn't a frivolous one. Hardy seems to share the ambiguous attitude to insect-life displayed by many of his characters: on the one hand the friendly anthropomorphism of 'An August Midnight', where the 'sleepy fly that rubs its hands' is greeted as 'my guest'; on the other the blighting comparisons which take it for granted that a human being reduced to the level of an ant or a cheese-mite is reduced indeed.

A possible explanation of this ambiguity lies in the recurrent emphasis, in relevant descriptions, on two apparently unrelated factors. One, already mentioned in passing, is the vividness of feeling attributed to the insects or associated with them. The ephemerons are 'heaving and wallowing with enjoyment', a wasp may be 'rolling drunk' or 'tipsy' (*Wood*, 136), the gnats 'wailing' or 'dancing up and down in airy companies' (*T-M*, 182). Cows, in *Tess* (151) jump 'wildly over the five-barred barton-gate, maddened by the gad-fly'. Mrs Charmond complains bitterly (*Wood*, 149) '"I lay awake last night, and I could hear the scrape of snails creeping up the window glass; it was so sad!"' Even in these smallest of nature's manifestations there is an intensity of life which serves to enlarge one's sense of the far greater intensity within the human protagonists.

The other repeated emphasis, already illustrated in the two passages from *Desperate Remedies*, is on vivid lighting effects. Insects become prominently visible in Hardy's novels in a context of illumination: 'singing insects hung in every sunbeam' (*Wood*, 224). It is because Marty South's house is in 'an exceptional state of radiance', that Percomb is able to see 'every now and then a moth, decrepit from the late season' (8). The night before he is posted away from Overcombe John Loveday sits in darkness by the mill-pond and peers up at Anne Garland's bedroom: 'The light shone out upon the broad and deep mill-head, illuminating to a distinct individuality every moth and gnat that entered the quivering chain of radiance...' (*T-M*, 173–4). Anne herself looks out at the scene 'for some time', but never guesses that John is there. During the period when Tess is prevaricating over the date of her wedding she often idles out of doors with Angel Clare:

> Looking over the damp sod in the direction of the sun a glistening ripple of gossamer-webs was visible to their eyes under the luminary, like the track of moonlight on the sea. Gnats, knowing nothing of their brief glorification, wandered across the shimmer of this pathway, irradiated as if they bore fire within them; then passed out of its line, and were quite extinct. In the presence of these things he would remind her that the date was still the question. (200)

The description and the situation are reminiscent of *Desperate Remedies* and *The Return of the Native*. Here, too, the implied metaphor is a comment on the brevity of human happiness and human life. The word 'irradiated' deserves some attention. In the otherwise subdued coda to *The Mayor of Casterbridge* the life of Elizabeth-Jane, now happily married to Farfrae, is described as 'suddenly irradiated'. After Tess has 'confessed' to Angel Clare they go for a miserable night walk. She notices that the stars are reflected in the small puddles of water created by the footprints of cattle: 'the vastest things of the universe imaged in objects so mean.' Clare, she knows, sees her 'without irradiation ... in all her bareness' (228). She has enjoyed no more that a 'brief glorification', like that of the gnats. The echoed word confirms that the 'radiance' recurrent in these descriptions is suggestive of a momentary joy and beauty. More mundanely, of course, the bright light is often necessary to enable the tiny insects to be seen at all – but it also dramatizes the significance to be inferred from their doings. It illuminates in more senses than one, and the observer may or may not like what is seen.

A Pair of Blue Eyes includes an episode that neatly illustrates the process. Shortly after Stephen Smith's return from India, at a time when he is still miserably uncertain about the state of Elfride's affections, he goes walking at night and hears her voice. He watches as she and a male companion enter a summer-house:

> The scratch of a striking light was heard, and a glow radiated from the interior of the building. The light gave birth to dancing leaf-shadows, lustrous streaks, dots, sparkles, and threads of silver sheen of all imaginable variety and transience. It awakened gnats, which flew towards it, revealed shiny gossamer threads, disturbed

earthworms. Stephen gave but little attention to these phenomena, and less time. He saw in the summer-house a strongly illuminated picture. (236)

As often in Hardy the sudden light in the darkness is both literal and metaphorical. Here the insects are incidental, their reactions a by-product of the 'illumination' that Elfride has transferred her affections to Smith's best friend. In several of the passages quoted earlier an unusual intensity of light serves solely to display or 'glorify' the insects, which provide a purely metaphorical revelation. As he gazes into the water-butt Manston sees 'with wonderful distinctness' not merely the ephemerons but a certain aspect of life. In Hardy terms he experiences a 'moment of vision'. What Smith is enabled to see tells him that he has lost his lover, but also hints to the reader, and perhaps subliminally to Smith himself, that this revelation is one manifestation of animal life among a myriad. The worms and gnats have concerns of their own. The gossamer threads, as in the passage from *Tess*, suggest the fragility of human hopes and aspirations.

A claim which must be reiterated at several points in this book is that Hardy's habit of metaphor suggests a peculiar density and mutuality of association. Repeatedly his imagery implies that any given aspect of nature partakes of others. In *Tess*, for example, cows are described as having teats 'as hard as carrots' (126); there is 'a monstrous pumpkin-like moon' (179); the heroine herself is likened to a bird, a cat, a sapling, a flower – as well as to a fly. Insects regularly feature in such comparisons. Birch trees are said to 'put on their new leaves, delicate as butterflies' wings' (*RN*, 389), cowslips seem to give out a light 'as from... glow-worms' (*Life*, 112), children in school are heard 'humming small, like a swarm of gnats' (*Jude*, 211). Frequently such images, or implied images, seem to involve not mere similitude, but assimilation. The things or creatures compared are seen to display virtually a common characteristic, or to engage in virtually a common activity. In *Two on a Tower* Hardy describes a Sunday-morning scene amid a blaze of spring flowers:

The animate things that moved amid this scene of colour were plodding bees, gadding butterflies, and numerous sauntering young feminine candidates for the impending confirmation, who, having gaily bedecked themselves for the ceremony, were enjoying their own appearance by walking about in twos and threes till it was time to start. (173)

The girls here seem not essentially distinguishable from the 'gadding butterflies': both species wander in the sunshine, delighting in self-display.

In *The Woodlanders*, when Fitzpiers has just made his first clear advances to Grace Melbury, there is a sudden diversion: 'two large birds ... apparently engrossed in a desperate quarrel' tumble into the hot ashes of an open-air fire and singe their wings. ' "That's the end of what is called love!"' observes Marty South, who happens to be passing and has not seen Grace or Fitzpiers. Hardy is well below his best here. The symbol would seem extrinsic and contrived even without Marty's unlikely interpretative intervention. The effect apparently intended is more elegantly achieved by the poem 'The Moth-Signal' and the parallel episode (mentioned earlier) in *The Return of the Native*. In both cases Hardy is at pains to stress that the moth lured to the candle is 'burnt and broken', as will be the lover drawn to the flame. It is in the nature of the creatures described to connive, bedazzled, at their own destruction. The insect metaphor seems less forced in that the reactions of moth and lover are seen, impartially, as instinctual.

When Anne Loveday watches the *Victory* depart (*T-M*, 293) she sees it diminish until 'no more than a dead fly's wing on a sheet of spider's web'. Conversely *The Hand of Ethelberta* features a seaside prospect in which 'a white butterfly among the apple-trees might be mistaken for the sails of a yacht far away on the sea' (178). These complementary images represent a more orthodox version of the shift of perspective seen in the passage from the *Life*, and they make more than a visual point. The things ostensibly compared are in effect the *same* thing: the butterfly's wings function as sails; the sails of the ship are man-made wings.

There is a Darwinian implication here. Man and insect are fellow species, driven by similar impulses, struggling to survive with the capacities at their command, some of which they have in common. In our different ways, and perhaps for different ends, we shrink from the rain, bask in the sun, ride on the wind. Conflicts of interest can arise between our species, often fatal to the insects. In *The Woodlanders* Fitzpiers watches as three girls, Suke Damson, Marty South and Grace Melbury, cope, or fail to cope, with the challenge posed by a newly-painted gate. The first two soil their clothes; the more alert Grace pushes the sticky gate aside with a twig, and passes unscathed. The most unfortunate victims are the gnats which 'stuck dying thereon' (86). It could be argued that the gnats and the human passers-by are fellow-sufferers. On the other hand the problem concerned is one that men alone could cause and men alone could solve – as Grace does. Deliberately or involuntarily human beings can wreak havoc in the insect world. As Tess and her friends walk to Mellstock Church 'Their gauzy skirts had brushed up from the grass innumerable flies and butterflies which, unable to escape, remained caged in the transparent tissue as in an aviary' (146). Paula Power stands by the fire (*Lao*, 185) and notices 'the wood-lice which ran out from beneath the bark to the extremity of the logs, as the heat approached them'. The mill in *The Trumpet-Major* is the home of the Lovedays, of the Garlands – and also of a variety of insects and other small creatures. Some of these fall victim to the human inhabitants. The Miller and his son Bob talk of the ubiquitous brown and black slugs, and 'of the relative exterminatory merits of a pair of scissors and the heel of the shoe' (155). The great clean-up which precedes Matilda's arrival inflicts carnage: 'The upper floors were scrubbed with such abundance of water that the old-established death-watches, wood-lice and flour-worms were all drowned ...' (131).

Insects, however, are capable of making encroachments on their own account. In Bathsheba Everdene's house the floorboards have been 'eaten into innumerable vermiculations' (76). The very cupboards Mrs Garland is cleaning are 'worm-eaten' – as, eventually, will be the pikes of the local militia (196 and Preface). Man and insect are locked willy-nilly into a scheme of mutual depredation. The oak coffer where Miller Loveday has kept his wardrobe encloses a 'hard stratification of old jackets, waistcoats, and knee-breeches at the bottom, never disturbed since the miller's wife died, and half pulverized by the moths, whose flattened skeletones lay amid the mass in thousands' (132). The moths have destroyed the clothes; the clothes have crushed the moths: there remains a powdery precipitate of lifeless matter.

In a passage from *The Return of the Native* already referred to, Clym Yeobright, furze-cutting on the heath, is said to be 'fretting its surface in his daily labour as a moth frets a garment' (279). Again the encroachments are reciprocal: later the heath will in its own way devour his wife and mother. The biblical phrase recurs near the end of *The Well-Beloved* (in both versions), when Marcia has shown Pierston her now elderly face devoid of make-up: ' "I am sorry if I shock you ... But the moth frets the garment somewhat in such an interval." ' (200) As in the Old Testament, the image is of the stealthy erosion of beauty by natural processes. The preceding paragraph has proposed a harsher series of metaphors: 'To this the face he once kissed had been brought by the raspings, chisellings, scourgings, bakings, freezings of forty invidious years ...'. 'Raspings' and 'chisellings' are resonant words in a novel centrally concerned with sculpture. Stone itself is not immune to such 'fretting'. We have seen how the very rock on which the main characters dwell has been cut up by saws to provide the raw materials for houses, churches, statues.

Stone of various kinds is another recurrent element in Hardy's fiction, often serving to image an enduring strength that yields with extreme reluctance to time yet is emptily insentient. Insects are insignificant, ephemeral to near-invisibility, the very slightest emanation of life – yet can be touched with joy or glory in their brief existences. The fossilized trilobite in *A Pair of Blue Eyes* is in Hardyesque terms a kind of far-fetched pun. Whatever the tribulations or ecstasies of its original life it has survived for millions of years, but without further 'irradiation'. In their different ways, on their different time-scales, rock and insect represent the process of change and evolution in which the human players are also trapped. Because that very process is intrinsic to Hardy's view of life the ant, the caterpillar and the gnat are far from incidental elements in his descriptions of nature.

3
Noises in Hardy's Novels

Hardy's fiction, like Prospero's island, is full of noises. Some are straight-forwardly musical – produced by singers, solo instrumentalists, church bells, dance-bands. Hardy's interest in music, of course, is very much a topic in its own right – a topic which has been widely discussed. Many of his leading characters are musicians of a sort: Christopher Julian is a composer, Dick Dewy and Donald Farfrae are singers, Oak plays the flute, Manston the organ, John Loveday the trumpet, Angel Clare the harp. Repeatedly music is shown to have a powerful influence on emotional life. Stephen Smith falls in love with Elfride as she sings to him at the piano. Elizabeth-Jane is moved by Farfrae's singing, Tess by Angel's harp-playing. Cytherea is reduced to the Hardyesque state of 'fascination' when Manston plays the organ for her during a storm.

The extremest case of this kind is the relationship between Car'line Aspent and Mop Ollamoor in 'The Fiddler of the Reels'. Mop, who can maliciously reduce children to tears by his playing, fascinates Car'line to the point of abjection. His playing makes her laugh and weep simultaneously. It has the power of 'projecting through her nerves excruciating spasms, a sort of blissful torture' (*Complete Stories*, 471) and eventually inducing convulsions. At one stage in their relationship even the sound of his footfall, by association, can make her 'start from her seat in the chimney-corner as if she had received a galvanic shock, and spring convulsively towards the ceiling' (462). Hardy remarks that it would require a neurologist to explain such reactions.

The story seems the more substantial in the light of his acknowledge-ment in the *Life* that some of the dance tunes his father played to him when he was a child would regularly move him to tears. He admits that 'he danced on at these times to conceal his weeping': 'This peculiarity in himself troubled the mind of "Tommy" as he was called, and set him wondering at a phenomenon to which he ventured not to confess' (19). Hardy names several of the melodies concerned, and it is intriguing to speculate why these apparently jaunty tunes should have moved him in this way. But such speculation would belong in a chapter, or book, exclusively devoted to music: this discussion is about noises at large. Music has been invoked chiefly to make the general point that Hardy thought of sound as a mysterious invasive force capable of slipping past one's intellectual defences and interfering unaccountably with the emotions.

The first concern of this chapter is natural and incidental sound, as of wind, rain, thunder, flowing water, animals, birds, insects, clocks, machinery, vehicles, footsteps, banging doors. Such effects are so common in Hardy's fiction as to become a significant narrative element, a sort of invisible 'stuff'. If, as has often been claimed, his novels are cinematic, such noises provide a soundtrack.

Joan Grundy sums up the importance of sound to Hardy when she observes: '... hearing being, equally with seeing, a mode of perception, Hardy's rendering of the external world is made as much in terms of the auditory, of *natural* music, as it is in terms of the visual.'[1] It comes instinctively to him to depict a scene partly, sometimes even wholly, through what meets the ear. The technique can be relatively straightforward when *work* is involved. The Durnover district of Casterbridge echoes 'with the thump of the flail, the flutter of the winnowing-fan, and the purr of the milk into the pails' (*MC*, 92). The smell of newly cut swedes at Flintcomb-Ash is 'accompanied by the sounds of the snuffling wind, the smart swish of the slicing-blades, and the choppings of the hook in Tess's leather-gloved hand' (*Tess*, 305). More surprisingly Hardy can provide a diverse aural background for a polite tea-party. Lucetta is playing hostess to both Farfrae and Henchard:

there were long spaces of taciturnity, when all exterior circumstance was reduced to the touch of spoons and china, the click of a heel on the pavement under the window, the passing of a wheelbarrow or cart and the whistling of the carter, the gush of water into householders' buckets at the town-pump opposite; the exchange of greetings among these neighbours, and the rattle of the yokes by which they carried off their evening supply. (*MC*, 182)

This description is one of many in Hardy's fiction evoking that familiar state of heightened awareness in which sounds become preternaturally prominent. Sometimes, as here, the cause of this awareness – for example, embarrassment or tension – is the central concern; but often such awareness seems to be invoked as an excuse for dwelling on the sounds. It is common practice with Hardy to begin a scene with a panoramic description before focusing on what is to prove relevant to the emerging story. If the observing character is in listening mood the 'panorama' can be acoustic:

> Every sound could be heard for miles. There was a great crowing of cocks, bleating of sheep, and cawing of rooks, which proceeded from all points of the compass, rising and falling as the origin of each sound was near or far away. There were also audible the voices of the people in the village, interspersed with hearty laughs, the bell of a distant flock of sheep, a robin close at hand, vehicles in the neighbouring roads and lanes.
>
> ('An Indiscretion in the Life of an Heiress', 56)

> The evening was so still that every trifling sound could be heard for miles. There was the rattle of a returning waggon, mixed with the smacks of the waggoner's whip: the team must have been at least three miles off. From far over the hill came the faint periodic yell of kennelled hounds; while from the nearest village resounded the voices of boys at play in the twilight. Then a powerful clock struck the hour...
>
> (*Lao*, 11)

The parallelism between these passages is structural, not merely verbal. Hardy creates an opportunity to provide a selective inventory: 'every...sound could be heard for miles. There was/were...'. He appeals to a natural human tendency to try to make sense, if only subconsciously, of anything that is heard. Here the mixture of noises of varying volume and proximity is traced back to particular sources, comprehending a variety of voices – animal and human – social life, moving vehicles. In both cases a solitary auditor takes in the soundscape quite casually, not knowing that from this confusion of impressions one will emerge into prominence to herald a great change in his life. At this relatively simple level the sound-picture serves as a sketch of the multifarious contingent detail from and amidst which the individual life takes shape.

Hardy's descriptions of isolated sounds are typically more emphatic and exact. Here is a brief selection of examples from a single novel, *Far from the Madding Crowd*:

He ... heard the crack-voiced cock-pheasants' 'cu-uck, cuck', and the wheezy whistle of the hens. (46)

There was not a sound of life save that acme and sublimation of all dismal sounds – the bark of a fox, its three hollow notes being rendered at intervals of a minute with the precision of a funeral bell. (275)

Every window replied by a clang to the opening and shutting of every door, a tremble followed every bustling movement, and a creak accompanied a walker about the house like a spirit, wherever he went. (76)

The church clock struck eleven. The air was so empty of other sounds that the whirr of the clockwork immediately before the strokes was distinct, and so was also the click of the same at their close. The notes flew forth with the usual blind obtuseness of inanimate things – flapping and rebounding among walls, undulating against the scattered clouds, spreading through their interstices into unexplored miles of space. (219)

Indoors nothing was to be heard save the droning of the blue-bottle flies: out of doors the whetting of scythes and the hiss of tressy oatears rubbing together as their perpendicular stalks of amber yellow fell heavily to each swath. (228)

A startling quiet overhung all surrounding things – so completely, that the crunching of the waggon-wheels was as a great noise, and small rustles, which had never obtained a hearing except by night, were distinctly individualised. (292)

What do such passages show? Most obviously that Hardy was exceptional, even among Victorian novelists, for the intensity with which he could imagine a scene, whether an indoor or an outdoor one, having it as vividly present to his ears as to his eyes. Moreover the sounds are heard and recorded with fastidious care – as one would expect of a musically-trained writer who troubled himself to take down 'the exact sound of the song of the nightingale', and who observed, in Venice, that the bell of the San Marco campanile had 'exactly that tin-tray *timbre* given out by the bells of Longpuddle and Weatherbury, showing that they are of precisely the same proportioned alloy' (*Life*, 59 and 200). The recurring insistence on 'precision' or 'exactness' is notable and persuasive. Hardy goes to corresponding trouble to try and reproduce the sounds verbally; hence the thoughtfully chosen nouns – 'clang', 'creak', 'whirr', 'click' – and the onomatopoeic phrasing: 'the hiss of tressy oat-ears'.

One virtue of this aural emphasis, from the narrative point of view, is its immediacy. Even though a story is formally told in the past tense sounds happen in the present: we hear them *now*.

> And in the dead silence which followed ... the breathings of the man and of the woman could be distinctly and separately heard. And there was this difference between them. His respirations gradually grew quieter and less rapid after the enunciation: hers, from having been low and regular increased in quickness and force till she almost panted. (*UGT*, 171)

This scrupulous account of the sounds that follow Maybold's proposal of marriage places the reader directly within that wordless interlude. We hear the breathings; we feel the tension. In *The Profitable Reading of Fiction* Hardy remarks that: 'In pursuance of a quest for a true exhibition of man, the reader will naturally consider whether he feels himself under the guidance of a mind who sees further into life than he himself has seen ...' (*Personal Writings*, 115). One of the ways in which Hardy earns such authority is by repeatedly demonstrating an extraordinarily acute physical sensitivity. He hears more and sees more than most of us, and offers us the benefit of those abilities. When reading his novels one is granted, as in *The Dynasts*, 'enlarged powers of audition as of vision' (*Dynasts*, 354). We are enabled to hear, for example, the minute sounds made by clothing: 'the scratching of silk over stubble' (*TT*, 110), 'the brushing of her dress and his gaiters against the heather' (*HE*, 7). So acute is Hardy's own ear that he is impelled to record not only sounds, but modifications of sounds. In *Far from the Madding Crowd* he notes how a sheep bell is partly muffled by 'an increasing growth of surrounding wool' (16), and a church bell by an overlay of snow (89). On occasion he will even strain to suggest the distortion of sound by space:

> 'Eno-o-o-o-ch!' cried Dick at the top of his voice.
> 'Y-a-a-a-a-as!' said Enoch from the distance.

'D'ye know who I be-e-e-e-e?'
'No-o-o-o-o-o-o!' (*UGT*, 191)

So an essential preliminary comment on Hardy's mastery of sound is that it contributes substantially to the vividness of the narrative, and enhances the authority of the narrator. He *hears* the scenes he invents and the countryside he knows so well, and can enable his readers to hear likewise. If the compliment is obvious it is far from negligible, bearing, as it does, on the essential imaginative life of his fiction, on Hardy's ability to locate us in a working model of an inexhaustibly vital and volatile world.

II

At first glance this gift would seem to be an uncomplicated aspect of realism; but further study shows it be something more far-reaching. Attentive reading of *Desperate Remedies* suggests that Hardy was consciously intrigued, from the start of his novelistic career, by the psychology of aural response. Chapter Six, the account of Cytherea's first night at Knapwater House, is a particularly extravagant passage of storytelling with the intriguing rotten-ripeness of some wicked old cheese. At the heart of it is the scene where Cytherea, unexpectedly in bed with her sensual new mistress, lies awake tormented by mysterious sounds – in the first instance 'a strange and gloomy murmur':

> She recognized it: it was the gushing of the waterfall, faint and low, brought from its source to the unwonted distance of the House by a faint breeze which made it distinctly perceptible by reason of the utter absence of all disturbing noises. The groom's melancholy representation lent to the sound a more dismal effect than it would have had of its own nature. She began to fancy what the waterfall must be like at that hour, under the trees in the ghostly moonlight. Black at the head, and over the surface of the deep cold hole into which it fell; white and frothy at the fall; black and white, like a pall and its border; sad everywhere. (119–20)

The sound concerned is the first in a sequence of five. Hardy's comments on it bear on the very nature of listening. Cytherea feels compelled to interpret what she hears and then to visualize the phenomena that seem to have produced the sound. Recalling the groom's comment – ' "There's something awful in the unending o' that sound, ain't there, miss?" '(93) – she paints a gloomy mental picture. Having done so she is 'in the mood for sounds of every kind', and another soon comes:

> a kind of intermittent whistle it seemed primarily: no, a creak, a metallic creak, ever and anon, like a plough, or a rusty wheelbarrow, or at least a wheel of some kind. Yes, it was a wheel – the water-wheel in the shrubbery by the old manor-house, which the coach-man had said would drive him mad. (120)

Again she strives to identify the sound, this time through a series of progressively closer guesses. Again she is driven to visualize: 'To imagine the inside of the engine-house, whence these noises proceeded, was now a necessity'. As before, her imaginings, coloured by the coachman's reaction, have a Gothic flavour. She frightens herself enough to shiver.

When the third sound comes, therefore, the reader, equally with Cytherea, is eager to decipher it and predisposed to find it sinister. Like her we grope in the dark. Hardy makes the most of his opportunity to tease. This noise, close at hand, 'a very soft gurgle or rattle', is one which Cytherea thinks she has heard before – yet she still cannot place it. It sets the dogs barking. In a moment Miss Aldclyffe wakes, with a low scream, from a nightmare, and the sequence is complete.

We later learn that the sound in question was the death-rattle of Captain Bradleigh, Miss Aldclyffe's father, who had perhaps been fin-ished off by his birthday party of the previous evening. From the point of view of plot Cytherea could have been allowed a dreamless sleep, since the unfortunate old gentleman would still have been found dead next morning if she had never heard a thing. As earlier in the novel – most obviously in the account of Mr Graye's death – Hardy is under-standably doing his best to instil tension and melodrama into the enabling episodes of a mystery story yet to get into its stride. But it is interesting that he does so in this particular instance by drawing on human impulses that are to loom large in his work in more serious contexts: the impulse to listen, to be imaginatively stirred by what one hears, to try to make sense of it, to distil a mood from it. The passage is effective – which in the context of *Desperate Remedies* needn't mean more than that it's fun to read – because we are in the same position as Cytherea. We have all the information she has, and we react in the same way, sharing her imaginings and trying to out-guess her.

Cytherea's predicament may be far-fetched, 'sensational', but the technique involved was to be employed time and again by Hardy. His leading characters tend to be solitaries, and many of the episodes in his fiction take place at night. It frequently happens, therefore, that he comes to describe an individual alone in the darkness, straining to convert a sound heard into a mental image. Another passage from *Far from the Madding Crowd* conveniently exemplifies this situation:

> Here the only sounds disturbing the stillness were steady munchings of many mouths, and stentorian breathings from all but invisible noses, ending in snores and puffs like the blowing of bellows slowly. Then the munching would re-commence, when the lively imagination might assist the eye to discern a group of pink-white nostrils, shaped as caverns, and very clammy and humid on their surfaces ... (169)

The sounds prompt the eye and the imagination assists it, with the effect that in the darkness the bovine nostrils effectively become a clearly-seen – 'pink-white' – and even a tactile presence. Since the 'lively imagination' referred to may be the writer's or the reader's equally with Bathsheba's the description can be taken as a demonstration of one aspect of the storyteller's craft – the aspect frequently misconstrued, in critical argument, as a hopeless attempt to 'represent reality'. Just as Bathsheba is able to discern the heads of the 'all but invisible' cows so the reader has been induced to 'see', almost to touch, something that does not exist. There is a related comment in *The Return of the Native*, in a chapter appropriately entitled 'How a Little Sound produced a Great Dream'. Eustacia, desperate to meet the newly-returned Clym Yeobright, happens to pass him in the dusk when he is out with Thomasin and his mother:

> She strained her eyes to see them, but was unable. Such was her intentness, however, that it seemed as if her ears were performing the functions of seeing as well as hearing. (115)

This comment, like several of those quoted earlier, shows Hardy's habitual readiness to translate one kind of sensual impression into another. Only a few chapters earlier Eustacia and Wildeve have responded in this way to a mournful wind:

> Compound utterances addressed themselves to their senses, and it was possible to view by ear the features of the neighbourhood. Acoustic pictures were returned from the darkened scenery ... (82)

Later in the novel Clym, likewise, as his sight grows worse, is forced to deduce sights from sounds:

> The life of this sweet cousin, her baby, and her servants, came to Clym's senses only in the form of sounds through a wood partition as he sat over books of exceptionally large type; but his ear became at last so accustomed to these slight noises from the other part of the house that he could almost witness the scenes they signified. A faint beat of half-seconds conjured up Thomas in rocking the cradle, a wavering hum meant that she was singing the baby to sleep, a crunching of sand as between millstones raised the picture of Humphrey's, Fairway's, or Sam's heavy feet crossing the stone floor of the kitchen, a light step, and a gay tune in a high key, betokened a visit from Grandfer Cantle, a sudden break-off in the Grandfer's utterances implied the application to his lips of a mug of small beer, a bustling and slamming of doors meant starting to go to market...
> (387–8)

Only in a superficial sense is Clym's disability the centre of interest. Here Hardy make the character's near-blindness, as elsewhere he makes darkness, an excuse for presenting a sound-picture. Descriptively the device is ingenious. The author provides a thumb-nail sketch of a way of life, and achieves an extra edge of vividness by making us hear what he simultaneously induces us to visualize. At the same time a trick has been played. The reader, like the characters concerned, has been enabled to see in the dark – or at least to feel that something like this happened. The subtext may be that this is how description works in fiction. We cannot be 'shown' a scene, but we can be enabled and persuaded to create our own pictures, very much as Clym does.

III

Many of the noises in Hardy's novels are plainly included less for the sake of descriptive density than for thematic reasons. Among these are the sounds made by dying animals in *Tess* and *Jude*: for example, Prince's 'groan' and the 'hiss' of his blood as he dies, the 'gasp or gurgle' of the dying pheasants (*Tess*, 36, 270), the 'shrill squeak' of the trapped rabbit (*Jude*, 224). When Jude and Arabella set about killing their pig it goes through a gamut of vocal reactions. Its 'squeak of surprise' gives way to 'repeated cries of rage', later to 'the cry of despair; long-drawn, slow and hopeless', and finally to 'the shriek of agony'

(63–4). The hints here are plain enough: the sounds derive from a sustained metaphor. Tess and Jude, too, are tormented animals, eventually hounded to death. They have the stoicism of most of Hardy's characters; the animals who stand in for them, metaphorically, are made to squeak or shriek on their behalf. The reference to the pig as Jude's 'fellow-mortal' is hardly necessary.

There are many such indirect aural metaphors in Hardy's fiction, usually less obvious in their implications. Among them is the sound (mentioned in a previous chapter) that troubles Mrs Charmond: ' "I lay awake last night, and I could hear the scrape of snails creeping up the window-glass; it was so sad!"' (*Wood*, 149). In effect that image is glossed by a later, purely visual, one:

> The early morning of this day had been dull, after a night of wind, and on looking out of the window in the grey grim dawn Fitzpiers had observed some of Melbury's men dragging away a large limb which had been snapped off a beech tree. Everything was cold and colourless.
>
> 'My good God!' he said as he stood in his dressing-gown. 'This is life!' (166)

Fitzpiers sees, as Mrs Charmond hears, something that can be interpreted as a meanness or futility in nature – something that by analogy blights their own sense of purpose. Clym Yeobright could be speaking for Mrs Charmond when he says, shortly after his mother's death: 'I can do nothing. My life creeps like a snail' (*RN*, 323). In the passage from *The Woodlanders* the same comparison is present but is left unexplained. Everywhere in Hardy nature offers a commentary on the doings of mankind, and the sounds of nature help to dramatize it.

This commentary, in itself and in its aural aspect, is usually far more diffused and ambiguous in its effect than the animal cries referred to above. Hardy's apparently incidental descriptions of sound contribute to a sustained meditation about man's place in the scheme of things. The parallel passages quoted at the start of this chapter present a promiscuous mingling of the noises of nature and the noises of people. The association implies a fundamental similarity between them. Hardy often makes the same point by means of comparison, direct or indirect. Maybold's nervous rapping at the door is 'no louder than the tapping of a distant woodpecker' (*UGT*, 170); the barking-tool used by Melbury's men makes a sound 'something like the quack of ducks'

(*Wood*, 102); reeds of a certain kind produce 'sounds as of a congrega-
tion praying humbly' (*RN*, 39).

> Sustained snores came from the cart-house, where some of the men
> were lying down; the grunt and squeal of sweltering pigs arose from
> the still further distance. (*Tess*, 171)

Nature makes noises; Man makes noises. Hardy often suggests that
the former statement includes, and perhaps sufficiently explains, the
latter – as, for example, in the account of the birth of the third Avice:

> The sea moaned – more than moaned – among the boulders below the
> ruins, a throe of its tide being timed to regular intervals. These sounds
> were accompanied by an equally periodic moan from the interior of
> the cottage chamber; so that the articulate heave of water and the
> articulate heave of life seemed but differing utterances of the selfsame
> troubled terrestrial Being – which in one sense they were. (*W-B*, 132)

A paragraph later the point is underlined by a reference to 'the travail
of the sea without, and the travail of the woman within'. The sea and
the woman are seen as involuntarily expressing, in their different ways,
the energies of a single life-force. Incidentally, there is a revealing con-
sistency in the fact that Hardy's first novel highlights the sounds of
death and his last one the sounds of birth.

In many passages the tacit comparison seems carried to the level of
the mutual assimilation described in the previous chapter. The morning after opening Fanny's coffin Bathsheba, who has rushed out into
the darkness, is awakened and progressively soothed by a sequence of
natural noises:

> A coarse-throated chatter was the first sound.
> It was a sparrow just waking.
> Next 'Chee-weeze-weeze-weeze!' from another retreat.
> It was a finch.
> Third: 'tink-tink-tink-tink-a-chink!' from the hedge.
> It was a robin.
> 'Chuck-chuck-chuck!' overhead.
> A squirrel.
> Then, from the road, 'With my ra-ta-ta, and my rum-tum-tum!'
> It was a ploughboy. (*FMC*, 313)

These are cheerful morning sounds that do much to revive Bathsheba's spirits. In this context the ploughboy's song seems as natural and instinctive as the finch's – the more so in that he is singing merely a refrain made up of vocables. Like the sleeping men at Talbothays or the woman in labour on the Isle of Slingers he is just another noise-making animal – and so, by inference, are the rest of us.

It's worth noting, however, that the boy's case might be thought to differ from the other two in that he is making music. The term has an equivocal meaning in Hardy's work. In Chapter Two of the same novel, after an extended account of the 'music' of the wind on Norcombe Hill the author seems to claim that the music of man is different in kind:

> Suddenly an unexpected series of sounds began to be heard in this place up against the sky. They had a clearness which was to be found nowhere in the wind, and a sequence which was to be found nowhere in nature. They were the notes of Farmer Oak's flute. (*FMC*, 14)

The comment seems all of a piece with Hardy's recurrent emphasis on the uniqueness of Man as a thinking animal. On this view we alone create music, exercising invention and control, as opposed to merely making noises. Conversely the random sounds of nature can be described as 'musical' only to the extent that we choose, or feel obliged, so to interpret them.

> The instinctive act of human-kind was to stand, and listen, and learn how the trees on the right and the trees on the left wailed or chanted to each other in the regular antiphonies of a cathedral choir; how hedges and other shapes to leeward then caught the note, lowering it to the tenderest sob … (*FMC*, 14)

The sounds become 'antiphonies' when they are heard as such by the thinking human listener. Hardy offers an oblique further comment on this notion a couple of paragraphs later. He concludes a magnificent description of the stars, conveying a physical sense of the world's progress through them, with the observation: 'After such a nocturnal reconnoitre it is hard to get back to earth, and to believe that the consciousness of such majestic speeding is derived from a tiny human frame'. Hardy readers will recognize a favourite and recurring paradox. In the scheme of creation the individual life is of infinitesimal significance, yet creation itself arguably exists only to and through the individual human mind. Even the movements of the stars become 'majestic' only because we are here to devise and apply the term. Our very capacity to apprehend humanity's unimportance in the larger scheme of things is an attribute of a consciousness startlingly unique.

In relation to sound, however, the paradox is compounded. Despite the comment on Oak's flute-playing Hardy habitually describes nature's noises in musical terms:

> The wanderer in this direction, who should stand still for a few moments on a quiet night, might hear singular symphonies from these waters, as from a lampless orchestra, all playing in their sundry tones, from near and far parts of the moor. At a hole in a rotten weir they executed a recitative; where a tributary brook fell over a stone breastwork they trilled cheerily; under an arch they performed a metallic cymbaling; and at Durnover-Hole they hissed. (*MC*, 296)

> The wind, playing upon the edifice, produced a booming tune, like the note of some gigantic one-stringed harp. (*Tess*, 379)

> Gusts in innumerable series followed each other from the northwest, and when each one of them raced past the sound of its progress resolved into three. Treble, tenor and bass notes were to be found therein...Next could be heard the baritone buzz of a holly tree. Below these in force, above them in pitch, a dwindled voice strove hard at a husky tune...
>
> Throughout the blowing of these plaintive November winds, that note bore a great resemblance to the ruins of human song which remain to the throat of fourscore and ten. It was a worn whisper, dry and papery, and it brushed so distinctly across the ear that, by the accustomed, the material minutiae in which it originated could be realised as by touch...
>
> They were the mummied heath-bells of the past summer, originally tender and purple, now washed colourless by Michaelmas rains, and dried to dead skins by October suns. (*RN*, 51)

The last example is quoted at greater length because it is so diversely characteristic of Hardy's complex response to the sounds of nature. A mood is evoked (the winds are 'plaintive') but the passage is fastidiously literal as to physical factors involved – the holly-tree, the dry heath-bells. There is a musician's exactitude in the placing of the 'notes': 'treble...tenor...bass...baritone...pitch'. Sound translates, as often in Hardy, into 'touch' and sight. Yet some aspects of what is imaginatively 'seen' by auditor and reader no longer exist: the purple colour disappeared months previously. Involved in the listening experience is a sense of passing time, 'Michaelmas rains...October suns': the sound is a distillation of memories. Each heath-bell, once colourful and 'tender', is in its dotage – the equivalent of 'fourscore and ten'. Somehow this transition becomes an aspect of what is heard. It is as though the heath-bells were feebly lamenting the brevity of their own existence. Through such associations Hardy implicitly accounts for the plaintiveness he refers to.

Eventually the extended description becomes an indirect comment on Eustacia's mood. Her long sigh

> ...was but as another phrase of the same discourse as theirs. Thrown out on the winds it became twined in with them, and with them it flew away. (*RN*, 52)

Eustacia's sigh is seen as a modest contribution to the wind itself. The girl, the Heath and the breeze would seem to share a common melancholy. But her sigh is surely as different in kind from the sounds of Nature as is Oak's flute-playing: the sadness is consciously experienced and rationally explicable. In a very similar passage from *Tess* Hardy makes the distinction clear. As the Durbeyfield wagon is driven through the darkness Abraham falls asleep:

> With no longer a companion to distract her, Tess fell more deeply into reverie than ever, her back leaning against the hives. The mute procession past her shoulders of trees and hedges became attached to fantastic scenes outside reality, and the occasional heave of the wind became the sigh of some immense sad soul, conterminous with the universe in space, and with history in time. (36)

Here it is plain that the element of pathetic fallacy derives from the consciousness of the unhappy Tess: it is an aspect of her fantastical reverie.

By analogy it would seem that Hardy's repeated references to the music to be found in nature can be no more than metaphorical. But the issue is complicated by the episode of the Aeolian harp, in *The Trumpet-Major*. This instrument, of course, repeatedly appears in Romantic poetry. Shelley begs the West Wind to 'Make me thy lyre, even as the forest is...' His Ode can be seen as an exemplification of that very possibility: Nature inspires him to produce a work of art. In 'The Eolian Harp' Coleridge ventures a bolder suggestion, instantly to be withdrawn as heterodox:

> ...what if all of animated nature
> Be but organic Harps diversely fram'd,
> That tremble into thought, as o'er them sweeps
> Plastic and vast, one intellectual breeze
> At once the Soul of each, and God of all?
>
> (ll. 44–8)

The context is a serene evening in which the harp is emitting 'a soft floating witchery of sound'. In 'Dejection' the mood and the weather produce a very different reaction:

> What a scream
> Of agony by torture lengthened out
> That lute sent forth! (ll. 97–9)

The wind has become a 'Mad Lutanist'. The Aeolian harp is an image tantalising in its ambiguity. Man makes it but the elements play it. Its sounds can be interpreted as the music of its maker or the music of Nature itself, or as some combination of the two.

Bob Loveday instals such an instrument in 'the keen damp draught' near the mill-head. When he uncovers it 'the wires began to emit a weird harmony which mingled curiously with the plashing of the wheel'. He tells Anne Garland that he has made it especially for her. Although she has resolved to repress her affection for him she finds herself touched:

> Every night after this, during the mournful gales of autumn, the strange mixed music of water, wind, and strings met her ear, swelling and sinking with an almost supernatural cadence. ...she marvelled pleasantly at the new depths of poetry this contrivance revealed as existent in that young seaman's nature, and allowed her emotions to flow out yet a little further in the old direction... (*T-M*, 183)

One particular night the sounds seem to shape themselves into the words ' "Remember me; think of me!" ' She finds them 'almost too touching'. Then Bob reveals that it was John, after all, who originally suggested the making of the 'queer noisy machine'. Thrown into confusion

Anne immediately asks Bob to take the instrument away. He undertakes to do so, but on the intervening night, when there happens to be a high wind:

> ...the harp cried and moaned so movingly that Anne, whose window was quite near, could hardly bear the sound with its new associations. John Loveday was present to her mind all night as an ill-used man; and yet she could not own that she had ill-used him. (184)

Is the melancholy merely in the ear of the auditor? Is it compounded by the accompanying 'music' from the timeless waters of the mill-stream? The human contribution is complex: it lies not only in the making of the instrument, but in the sensitivity of placing it in a particularly suitable spot, and in the feeling which prompts that sensitivity. For the listener there is a piquant mingling of sounds and of associations.

Anne is induced to respond in three quite distinct ways. First she reflects 'pleasantly' on the unexpected sensibility that has been revealed in Bob. Later the sounds become almost too expressive: presumably she hints that the harp should be removed because it is pleading too eloquently on Bob's behalf. It seems to reveal a new aspect of his personality. She attributes to his sensibility the emotions she reads into the music: 'You are poetical, Captain Bob'. But once she knows that the instrument speaks for John rather than his brother its cries and moans become almost unbearable, reminding her of the Trumpet-Major's hurt and her own complicity in it. In other words her interpretation of the music is strongly coloured by changing personal associations. The reader, who learns only when Anne does that the harp was John's idea, is left to reflect on the situation at large. There is an anticipation of *Cyrano de Bergerac* in this wooing by proxy. The sad music of the Aeolian harp can be taken as a lament for the pains and confusions of love in general.

Anne interprets the sounds variously, but only within a narrow spectrum of emotional possibilities. In *Far from the Madding Crowd* there is an account of river-noises 'which a sad man would have called moans, and a happy man laughter' (90) – and subjectivism of that kind is not uncommon in Hardy's novels. On the other hand the winds that play through the harp are not neutral forces but, it would seem unarguably, the 'mournful gales of autumn'. Again Hardy seems to suggest that the sounds of Nature are *intrinsically* expressive – not merely a reflection of the mood of the hearer – and that predominantly they are mournful sounds.

Certainly this is the view expressed by Marty South when she is tree-planting with Giles:

'How they sigh directly we put 'em upright, though while they are lying down they don't sigh at all,' said Marty.
'Do they?' said Giles. 'I've never noticed it.'
She erected one of the young pines into its hole, and held up her finger; the soft musical breathing immediately set in which was not to cease night or day till the grown tree should be felled – probably long after the two planters had been felled themselves.
'It seems to me,' the girl continued, 'as if they sigh because they are very sorry to begin life in earnest – just as we be.' (*Wood*, 50)

The passage is one of a number in Hardy's fiction containing sexual suggestion difficult to ignore and as difficult to decode,[2] but that oddity doesn't affect the essential meaning. Hardy suggests, through Marty, that at least to the sexually self-conscious – those who have begun life 'in earnest' – the world may be seen as a gigantic Aeolian Harp, whose ceaseless melodies must all be sad ones. John South shares, or comes to share, his daughter's view. The elm tree outside his cottage solicits his attention partly because of the 'sound of its sighs': '...he would sit all day, in spite of persuasion, watching its every sway, and listening to the melancholy Gregorian melodies which the air wrung out of it' (*Wood*, 70).

There is a tendency towards self-contradiction or even self-cancellation in such passages. Nature makes mournful music, presumably, in doleful acknowledgement of its own meaninglessness; but if it is indeed meaningless it cannot produce 'music' at all, merely random noises. The world is an Aeolian Harp only to the interpreting ears of humankind. Man is the sole music-maker and music-hearer.

An alternative position is that our very conception of music derives, after all, from the sounds of nature: the hearing precedes the patterning. In the *Life* Hardy quotes a comment he himself once made about some music by Wagner: 'It was *weather*- and ghost-music – whistling of wind and storm, the strumming of a gale on iron railings, the creaking of doors; low screams of entreaty and agony through key-holes...' (187). On this view Wagner, like the creators of 'Gregorian melodies', derives his art, ultimately, from the random sounds about him. If we interpret Nature as imitating art, musically speaking, the art that it mimics is itself an imitation of Nature.

IV

When Hardy speaks of the 'music' or 'songs' of nature, therefore, he is being instinctively equivocal. He offers the reader simultaneously the idea that our sense of the musicality of nature is subjective and delusive and the idea that our very conception of music is a methodizing of nature's sounds. There is a similar equivocation in his use of another favourite word, 'voice' – an equivocation he frequently exploits and explores. His poetry offers numerous examples. In 'The Voice of Things' the joyful 'huzza' of the waves is transformed, by the passing of twenty years to 'long ironic laughter'. The change, clearly, is in the disposition of the hearer. 'Voices from Things Growing in a Churchyard', as the very title suggests, implies a more complex view. There is a plurality of voices from a plurality of 'things' – and the things themselves are distinguishable as particular species of tree or flower. But their individuality goes further in that they are 'growing' from the bodies of the dead. Fancifully Hardy describes each of these speaking plants as providing an appropriate voice for the person buried in the grave below. Those deceased have been so gently transubstantiated as to remain in some sense vocal, speaking through the murmurings of the leaves they become. A poem that could sound, in description, too sweetly sentimental, avoids being so because the ostensible subject isn't the real one. Unlike Hardy's 'Friends Beyond' these 'maskers' are not individuals, affectionately recalled, but types. The poem is concerned with *general* issues. We often seek for messages from the dead; we regularly hear, or seem to hear, voices in the rustlings of twigs and foliage: might not the latter in some sense do duty for the former?

> All day cheerily,
> All night eerily!

The refrain – perhaps too glibly rhymed – asserts that any such relationship is in the head of the 'interpreter'. We hear genial messages in the cheerful daylight but sinister ones at night. On the other hand this subjective process does involve contact, of a kind, with the dead: the delusive 'accents' recall to the memory those who were known, and conjure up in the imagination those who are but names on a tombstone.

The dilemma is explored more pertinaciously in 'The Voice', where Hardy asks his late wife whether it is indeed she who is calling to him:

> Can it be you that I hear? Let me view you, then ...
> Or is it only the breeze in its listlessness
> Travelling across the wet mead to me here,

> You being ever dissolved to wan wistlessness,
> Heard no more again far or near?

Within the poem the question is only doubtfully answered, the single succeeding stanza being open to more than one possible reading. This ambiguity is compounded by the larger context. 'The Voice' is a response to its immediate predecessor in the sequence, 'The Haunter', from which it borrows, as demonstrable link, the ostentatious 'call to me/all to me' trisyllabic rhyme. 'The Haunter', of course, purports to be spoken by the ghost of Emma, which laments its inability to communicate with Hardy. By implication 'The Voice' is that of the ghost, after all faintly apprehended by the poet. Obviously this is not literally the case: Hardy has written both poems. He is questioning the status of a voice he hears in his imagination. But he is not merely playing a formal game, as the developing sequence proceeds to show. When he goes back to Cornwall 'to view a voiceless ghost' he finds Emma

> Facing round about me everywhere,
>   With your nut-coloured hair,
> And gray eyes, and rose-flush coming and going.

He is not 'really' seeing her; but the Emma of forty years previously has become physically alive in his memory again – and is, after all, (he proceeds to suggest) no less substantial than his own past self from the days when they 'haunted here together'. The voice he fancied he heard in the listless December wind would seem to have the equivocal substantiality of the face he sees with his mind's eye or of the younger Hardy whom he has been led to recollect.

The larger inference is that human beings are instinctively prone to hear voices in nature just as they see – or used to see – pictures in the fire. Or perhaps it's rather that our speech, like our music, can be seen as a dialect ultimately derived from the sounds of nature. We strive to distinguish familiar tones and cadences as we listen to the essentially unintelligible mother tongue.

V

In the area of sound, as in other aspects of Hardy's work, there is in interesting tension between realism and formalism. Many of the noises he describes are instantly familiar: we have all listened to winds or waters, or found ourselves aware of approaching footsteps or the ticking of a clock. Since Hardy invokes so much that we recognize, and recaptures it so vividly, it is natural to take on trust the many odder and subtler sounds he refers to – natural, but perhaps too simple. The night before giving, at a Hardy conference, the lecture from which this chapter originated, I went for a walk on a hillside near Dorchester. Since a breeze was blowing I listened conscientiously for some of the wind-effects I'd been making notes about, effects, I was prepared to claim, that Hardy recorded with astonishing precision. I listened in vain. It wasn't simply that I couldn't distinguish the voice of one tree from another: *no* voices were distinguishable. The noise of the wind itself, blowing past my ears, obliterated other sounds.

On reflection I didn't consider it an academic duty to compare my impressions with those of some keen-eared local forester. The wind-noises Hardy describes must be in some sense 'there'. Variously shaped, variously textured, branches, leaves and stems are bound to make individualised sounds in the breeze, even if human hearing can't distinguish them. The hyperbolical diversity implied can be found also in some of Hardy's visual descriptions:

> Further on were other tufts of moss in islands divided by the shed leaves – variety upon variety, dark green and pale green; moss like little fir-trees, like plush, like malachite stars; like nothing on earth except moss. (*Wood*, 378)

Similarly the accounts of the stars in *Two on a Tower* dramatize the paltriness of our physical perception. Swithin theorizes vertiginously about celestial multiplicities far beyond the capacities of our intellect or even our imagination. Hardy's aural descriptions have proved sufficiently plausible for the purposes of 'realism'. They haven't, as far as I know, been questioned or denounced by literalists. The more elaborately diverse of his acoustic pictures are perhaps intended to work primarily at the conceptual level, dramatizing the diversity and omnipresence of sound. Through intensification realism can invert itself into formalism as a fast-spun top can turn itself upside-down.

It is certainly true that Hardy often makes specifically formal use of sound. The ticking or chiming of clocks can be a choric reminder of the passing of time. So with the sound of running water: the stream at Overcombe Mill is described as 'stealing away, like Time' (*T-M*, 9). In 'The Waiting Supper' Nicholas and Christine regularly meet, over a period of years, by a waterfall, even though its 'sarcastic hiss' mocks their thwarted attempts to marry (*Complete Stories*, 565). Nicholas builds a cottage within earshot of 'the purl of the fall in the meadows, whose rush was a material rendering of Time's ceaseless scour over themselves, wearing them away without uniting them' (586). *The Well-Beloved,* another work which dwells on the passing of time and the erosion of bodies is punctuated by the 'articulate heave' of the sea and the grinding of pebbles. In *Tess* there is a patterning of sounds as of other motifs: one episode echoes, and so recalls, another. When the wind elicits from a Stonehenge monolith 'a booming tune, like the note of some gigantic one-stringed harp' (379) we recall the scene where Tess listened to Angel's playing. The 'Drip, drip, drip' of Alec's blood is a reprise of 'the measured dripping of the whey' from the cheese-wrings, a sound Tess repeatedly hears in the days when she is falling in love with Angel Clare.

In this adjustment between acute physical observation on the one hand, and formal patterning and conceptual exploration on the other, Hardy's fiction anticipates and resembles that of another musician, James Joyce. In *A Portrait of the Artist* the repeated registering of noises of various kinds both indicates Stephen's sensual responsiveness and helps to account for the nature of his evolving aesthetic ideas. The crashing of a cartload of old iron, a din that interrupts his theoretical monologue to Cranly, stands for the recalcitrant, uglier elements of experience that his aesthetic has yet to assimilate. Like Hardy Joyce starts from sound as raw sensual experience but moves towards abstract speculation about it.

The speculation is taken a good deal further in *Ulysses,* particularly, of course, in 'Sirens'. The episode offers a hyper-realistic inventory of sounds, ranging from an operatic aria to the click of a stick, the chink of coins, the picking of a thumbnail, laughter, farting and urination. At one level it questions literary convention: here is an acoustic *reductio ad absurdum* of epic comprehensiveness. Such sounds are present around us at every moment of our waking lives: what, if anything, are we to make of them all? At another level the chapter is a philosophical reverie about the evolution and the status of music. Dignified and undignified noises are shown to be close cousins. The winds and waters of the human body parody those of nature in the sounds they produce. Musical instruments, by implication, involve the arbitrary application of acoustic principles learned from common experience. Horse-hooves and clashing doors are percussive, a twanged garter is a type of the plucked string, Bloom, as he farts, becomes a wind instrument, and so on. The episode comprehends a hierarchy of sounds, from the barely audible to the cacophonous, from the touching to the grotesque, from grand opera to eructation, and implicitly puts the hierarchy in question.

These comments are intended as no more than a brief summary of the some of the issues touched upon in 'Sirens'. There has been no shortage of scholarly commentary on the chapter. My point is that the Hardy's concern with sound is in its way as 'philosophical' as Joyce's, if less obtrusively so. Like Joyce in 'Sirens' Hardy sometimes juxtaposes man's music with nature's:

> While he stood, the boom of the serpent within the adjacent house, and the lesser strains of the fiddler, reached the spot as an accompaniment to the surging hiss of the flying rain on the sod, its louder beating on the cabbage-leaves of the garden, on the straw hackles of eight or ten beehives just discernible by the path, and its dripping from the eaves into a row of buckets and pans that had been placed under the walls of the cottage. ('The Three Strangers', *Complete Stories*, 11)

Cabbage-leaves, beehives, buckets and pans could be mentioned merely for the sake of circumstantiality, but they variously modify the sound of the rain to make it a suggestive counterpoint to the melodies of serpent and fiddle. Here, as often, Hardy is obliquely reflecting on the nature of music very much as Joyce does.

There are other ways in which a 'realistic' aural description can be made to convey a Modernist subtext. It was suggested earlier that Hardy's characters – Clym nearly blind, Cytherea in the dark – often have to ask themselves 'What are these sounds? What do they mean?' As the acoustic descriptions multiply the reader may be led, subconsciously, to pose the same questions in philosophical terms: 'What *are* these sounds? What *do* they mean?' How do we make sense of the noises in our noise-ridden world?

Gillian Beer has intriguingly argued[3] that in his verse, at least, Hardy looks to physics for possible universalist explanations. She quoted 'In a Museum' and 'A Kiss' in particular as showing that Hardy was influenced by wave-theory. Both poems celebrate the survival of sound. In the former Hardy suggests that the prehistoric song of a bird now fossilized and a sweet contralto voice he has heard the previous day are, or will be, blended 'In the full-fugued song of the universe unending'. Similarly the kiss, from days long gone,

> cannot have died; that know we well.
> Somewhere it pursues its flight,
> One of a long procession of sounds
>   Travelling aethereal rounds
>   Far from earth's bounds
>   In the infinite.

Professor Beer suggests that in these poems Hardy invokes wave-theory as a counter to transience, rejecting what she called the 'Ode to a Nightingale' solution, which offers the consolation that although the song or the kiss has ended another bird, another contralto, another pair of lovers will take up the story. Also rejected, it may be said, (though it does feature in 'Shelley's Skylark') is the 'Grecian Urn' solution, which would see the lost figments immortalized in art. 'In a Museum' glances at yet another possibility, only to abandon it. The contralto's voice 'lodges in me still': it survives in the poet's recollection. But the most faithful memory, as the poet points out in 'Her Immortality', is less than a lifetime long.

Curiously the consolation proposed in the poems cited by Professor Beer scarcely features in Hardy's fiction. The nearest approach to it is probably to be found in the short story 'A Tryst at an Ancient Earthwork', a rare first-person narration:

> Acoustic perceptions multiply tonight. We can almost hear the stream of years that have borne those deeds away from us. Strange articulations seem to float on the air from that point, the gateway, where the animation in past times must frequently have concentrated itself at hours of coming and going, and general excitement. There arises an ineradicable fancy that they are human voices; if so, they must be the lingering air-borne vibrations of conversations uttered at least fifteen hundred years ago. (*Complete Stories*, 649)

Even here the fanciful quasi-scientific comment seems no more than a rhetorical elaboration of the more typically imaginative and superstitious response to the historic setting and the sounds of a stormy night. The argument of the two poems discussed by Professor Beer would seem to be one that Hardy the novelist hadn't considered, or hadn't found appealing.

Indeed the *kind* of consolation it offers would not seem likely to appeal to that earlier Hardy. Repeatedly, from *Desperate Remedies* onwards, he celebrates the particularity of the individual. Tess famously shrinks from the idea of being 'one of a long row only':

> 'The best is not to remember that your nature and your past doings have been just like thousands' and thousands', and that your coming life and doings'll be like thousands' and thousands'.' (130)

Cytherea, similarly, speaks with passion of her 'single opportunity of existence' (*DR*, 272). It seems unlikely that either of them would take comfort from wave-theory any more than from the 'Ode to a Nightingale'.

Hardy makes much of kissing in his novels. In terms of plot a kiss is often a turning point. In terms of theme it can mark the moment at which an idealized concept of love is first translated into physical reality. He therefore tends to describe kisses with some care – a care that can extend to their acoustic aspect:

> The gentle sounds around them from the hills, the plains, the distant town, the adjacent shore, the water heaving at their side, the kiss, and the long kiss, were all 'many a voice of one delight', and in unison with each another. (*DR*, 81)

> 'Come, kiss me,' repeated Miss Aldclyffe.
> Cytherea gave her a very small one, as soft in touch and in sound as the bursting of a bubble. (*DR*, 113)

> A kiss – not of the stealthy kind, but decisive, loud, and smart. (*PBE*, 70)

Appropriately Dick Dewy prepares for his first attempt to kiss Fancy Day by 'compressing his lips and pouting them out as if he were about to whistle the softest melody known' (*UGT*, 125). But in such cases the emphasis is again very much on the *now*. A single action, a single moment, registered in touch and perhaps in sound, can alter the course of two lives. The context and the instantaneity are crucial – and they inescapably imply transience. It seems unlikely that any of Hardy's fictional lovers, or indeed their creator, would find consolation for that transience in reflecting that the sound of the kiss had become an undetectable ingredient in a cosmic acoustic soup.

The view implied by 'In a Museum' is appropriately echoed in an entry in *The Life*:

> March 9. British Museum Reading Room. Souls are gliding about here in a sort of dream ... In the great circle of the library Time is looking into Space. Coughs are floating in the same great vault, mixing with the rustle of book-leaves risen from the dead, and the touches of footsteps on the floor. (215)

Characteristically Hardy offers the alternative, the individualized, response within three paragraphs:

> Footsteps, cabs, &c. are continually passing our lodgings. And every echo, pit-pat, and rumble that makes up the general noise has

behind it a motive, a prepossession, a hope, a fear, a fixed thought forward; perhaps more – a joy, a sorrow, a love, a revenge. (215)

VI

Hardy's instinctive interest in sound for its own sake is amply and miscellaneously displayed in *The Life*. Here are two illustrations:

'June 2. At Bockhampton. My birthday – 44. Alone in the plantation at 9 o'clock. A weird hour: strange faces and figures formed by dying lights … It is so silent and still that a footstep on the dead leaves could be heard a quarter of a mile off. Squirrels run up the trunks in fear, stamping and crying "chut-chut-chut".' (171–2)

'Evening. Just after sunset. Sitting with E. on a stone under the wall before the Refreshment Cottage. The sounds are two, and only two. On the left Durlstone Head roaring high and low, like a giant asleep. On the right a thrush. Above the bird hangs the new moon, and a steady planet. (111)

These are impressions that he took the trouble to record with some exactness and later chose to preserve for publication. Presumably they represent scenes that he instinctively felt to be in some sense significant – Moments of Vision or Joycean epiphanies. Visually Durlstone Head and the thrush are thrown into a triangular relationship with the moon, as the sounds of the two former presences are heard in the vast context of lunar silence. In both passages sound plays a prominent part but seems to interact with things seen. Both are enigmatic in their total effect. Again, like so many of the fictional extracts quoted in this chapter, they seem to invite interpretation. 'What *are* these noises? What makes them, and why? What do they mean?'

A preliminary gesture towards an explanation is the obvious claim that the noises in Hardy's novels, like the visual descriptions, are there to remind us that human beings are surrounded by contingent phenomena, overwhelming in scale and diversity, which are sometimes an influence on us, sometimes a distraction, always a source of information and analogy. More specifically – and this is a view which will be developed in succeeding chapters – sound stands for something beyond itself. It is produced by action, something happening, something being done. It affirms that we live in a world of endless, restless movement.

4
The Poetry of Motion

The noises pervading Hardy's fiction are regularly associated with movement. The numberless trees that variously sob, moan, hiss, rustle, whistle, whisper, grumble, moan, wail, chant, sigh, buzz, creak or rattle are being played upon by the wind, in which they as variously rock, quiver, sway, wave, battle or writhe. The second chapter of *Far from the Madding Crowd*, which begins with an extended sound-picture of this kind, is correspondingly full of references to the restlessness of the surrounding air (pp. 13–15):

> A desolating wind wandered from the north...

> ... the keenest blasts... smote the wood and floundered through it...

> ... the hurrying gust then plunged into the south to be heard no more.

> The wind continued to beat about the corners of the hut...

Trees, hedges, grasses and fallen leaves are all audibly agitated by the wind. But these familiar movements of air and vegetation are seen as types of a more general, even a universal, pattern of mobility. The very earth from which the trees grow is potentially unstable: even as he emphasizes the solidity of Norcombe Hill Hardy imagines a day 'when far grander heights and dizzy granite precipices topple down'. The heavens are visibly charged with activity:

> ... the twinkling of all the stars seemed to be but throbs of one body, timed by a common pulse.

> ... since evening the Bear had swung round..., till he was now at a right angle with the meridian. (14)

The Dog-star and Aldebaran, pointing to the restless Pleiades, were half way up the southern sky, and between them hung Orion which gorgeous constellation never burnt more vividly than now as it soared forth above the rim of the landscape. …the barren and gloomy square of Pegasus was creeping round to the north-west … (17)

These descriptive phrases, with their active verbs, provide a context for the startling paragraph on the 'majestic speeding' of our own planet – on our 'stately progress through the stars':

To persons standing alone on a hill during a clear midnight such as this, the roll of the world eastward is almost a palpable movement. The sensation may be caused by the panoramic glide of the stars past earthly objects, which is perceptible in a few minutes of still-ness; or by the better outlook on space that a hill affords, or by the wind; or by the solitude; but whatever be its origin the impression of riding along is vivid and abiding. (14)

Hardy earns the right to invoke, as he does, the phrase 'the poetry of motion'. He is depicting a scene of multiple, patterned activity. Leaves fall from trees which are shaken by wandering winds as the globe itself speeds through space amid countless throbbing, travelling stars. Sheep move and rustle in the darkness. Human beings are awake and working.

These opening pages of the chapter are easily read, and enjoyed, as a self-contained poetic interlude in Hardy's story, but they bear directly on the presentation of Gabriel Oak. His flute-playing, it was earlier sug-gested, is not merely at one with the natural context but makes a unique contribution to its acoustic life. He is shown to be similarly at home and at one with the movements of the night. He reads the time from the circling stars. Moreover in the pages that follow it is shown that he is not an observer, merely, but a participant in the choreogra-phy of the scene, as in its sounds. His shepherd's hut, 'on little wheels', is a mobile home, of a kind to be 'dragged into the fields when the lambing season comes on'. Only recently has he purchased his stock of sheep: the lambing he is engaged in is described as 'the first movement in his new progress'. His actual work, as discernible through the dark-ness, is also seen in terms of movement:

Oak's motions, though they had a quiet energy, were slow, and deliberateness accorded well with his occupation. Fitness being the basis of beauty, nobody could have denied that his steady swings and turns in and about the flock had elements of grace. Yet, although if occasion demanded he could do or think a thing with as mercurial a dash as can the men of towns who are more to the manner born, his special power, morally, physically, and mentally, was static, owing little or nothing to momentum as a rule. (16)

The sobriety of Hardy's tone disguises the unorthodoxy of defining a major character in terms of the tempo of his movements. Nor is the point made here an incidental one: it is to bear directly on the emerging story. Later this measured, 'static' quality in Oak, this relative lack of 'momentum', may be recollected in implicit contrast to the flashy speed and dexterity that Troy displays in the sword-play scene. For the time being his 'steady swings and turns' form a pattern of movement among other patterns of movement.

The paradox at the heart of the chapter, as has already been pointed out, is one that Hardy is to explore and exploit again and again. In this huge landscape and skyscape, unimaginably ancient and vast, alive with sound and movement, the workaday shepherd described in the opening chapter of the novel should surely seem negligible to the point of annihilation. Instead he is glorified – a participant in the vast processes of nature, but something much more. It is man alone whose sounds and movements are conscious and purposeful. It is man alone who interprets the scene and feels the wonder of it, man alone who can read a message in the stars yet admire their superlative beauty. The earth is unconscious of its own motion. The sense of its 'majestic speeding' derives from 'a tiny human frame'. Moreover on the human scale of values this same awe-inspiring vision can shrivel into inconsequence, as Hardy is to illustrate later in the novel in a passage concerning Bathsheba:

the unresting world wheeled her round to a contrasting prospect eastward, in the shape of indecisive and palpitating stars. She gazed upon their silent throes amid the the shades of space, but realized none at all. Her troubled spirit was far away with Troy. (218)

Our own 'throes', palpitations and indecisiveness can come to seem of incomparably greater moment than those of the stars. All we see we can mentally contain, explore, manipulate or subdue. In that perspective the quiet, unobtrusive shepherd, Gabriel Oak, is the dominating presence on Norcombe Hill.

II

The descriptions of the stars quoted above are typical in their emphasis. Hardy's skies seethe with life:

...the cold and clear March sky, its countless stars fluttering like bright birds. (*DR*, 355)

...the white stars twinkled so vehemently that their flickering seemed like the flapping of wings. (*UGT*, 11)

...above the wire rode the stars in their courses... (*Lao*, 21)

They were like those double stars which revolve round and round each other, and from a distance appear to be one. (*RN*, 241)

It was the silence and stillness of a starry sky, where all is force and motion. (*HE*, 136)

'Think of streams of satellites or meteors racing round and round the planet like a fly-wheel, so close together as to seem solid matter!' He entered further and further into the subject, his ideas gathering momentum as he went on, like his pet heavenly bodies. (*TT*, 31)

The metaphorical potentiality of descriptions such as these will be discussed later in this chapter. For immediate purposes what matters is that they serve as regular assertions that we inhabit a universe *intrinsically* mobile – defined and sustained by motion. It is important, indeed instinctive, to Hardy to show that all organisms, animate and inanimate, in different ways and at different speeds, are similarly caught up in endless movement.

In this spirit he describes winds of various kinds and intensities, shaking trees and buildings, rattling windows and lifting carpets. There are fierce gales, moderate breezes, insidious perturbations. At 'the Devil's Bellows', on Egdon Heath, 'when no perceptible wind was blowing the trees kept up a perpetual moan which one could hardly believe to be caused by the air' (*RN*, 280). The wind becomes the type of universal motion in Hardy. It can freshen a complexion, whisk away a hat, destroy a cottage, tear Pierston and Marcia apart 'as easily as coupled cherries' (*W-B*, 29). The young Jude Fawley apostrophizes in Marygreen the breeze that he calculates has been in Christminster less than two hours before. As Clym Yeobright crosses Egdon Heath 'Vapours from other continents arrived upon the wind, which curled and panted round him as he walked' (*RN*, 210).

More generally the novels are turbulent with weather. Clouds are borne along by the wind, shifting and bulging. Rain is flung violently through the air:

> The rain came down unmercifully, the booming wind caught it, bore it across the plain, whizzed it against the carriage like a sower sowing his seed. (*HE*, 276)

> The drops, which had at first hit their left cheeks like the pellets of a popgun, soon assumed the character of a raking fusillade... (*W-B*, 24)

> It was so high a situation, this field, that the rain had no occasion to fall, but raced along horizontally upon the yelling wind... (*Tess*, 278)

Hardy is notoriously at home with extremes of weather, such as a 'twanging and spinning storm' (*W-B*, 28), in which the whole skyscape explodes with energy. In *A Pair of Blue Eyes* he even contrives a scene in which the violent updraught of air against a cliff makes the rain 'fall' upwards.

His seas share the continual turmoil of his skies:

> Here strong currents and cross currents were beginning to interweave their scrolls and meshes, the water rising behind them in tumultuous heaps, and slamming against the fronts and angles of the cliff, whence it flew into the air like clouds of flour. (*HE*, 275)

In both versions of *The Well-Beloved* Hardy makes space for a full account of the treacherous Race: 'the confluence of the three currents making the surface of the sea at this point to boil like a pot...' (188). Even a tranquil evening scene at Sandbourne, in *The Hand of Ethelberta*, glitters with small shiftings, the countless movements of the water producing countless movements of light:

> The brilliant disc fired all the waves that lay between it and the shore at the bottom of the grounds, where the water tossed the ruddy light from one undulation to another in glares as large and clear as mirrors, incessantly altering them, destroying them, and creating them again; while further off they multiplied, thickened, and ran into one another like struggling armies, till they met the fiery source of them all. (*HE*, 29)

In a characteristic aside in *The Return of the Native* Hardy finds a yet more radical way of expressing the essential mobility of the sea: 'Distilled by the sun, kneaded by the moon, it is renewed in a year, in a day, or in an hour' (6).

The movements everywhere depicted by Hardy vary enormously in scale and pace. It is as though his universe is a huge machine in which the smallest of the interlocking wheels are almost invisible in the speed of their spinnings while the larger ones creep round barely perceptibly. At one extreme is the blast of a hurricane; at the other the virtually indiscernible shift of geological change. In the first chapter of *The Return of the Native* Hardy goes to great pains to establish the sense of permanence and sombre monotonousness of Egdon Heath. But seen in close-up at the right time of the year it is effervescent with ephemeral bustle, alive with rabbits, bees, grasshoppers and butterflies.

Hardy's descriptions of animal activity are too numerous and prominent to need illustration here. The earlier chapter on insects has already provided incidental examples of his interest in capturing with exactness the motions of particular creatures, the whizz of a crane-fly, the dancing of a gnat, the quivering of a butterfly. It was suggested there that the descriptions of clouds of gnats can be in effect a device for showing in minimally visual form the omnipresent vitality of nature. Equally typical are passages displaying the collective movement of creatures somewhat larger:

> A timid animal world had come to life for the season. Little tadpoles and efts began to bubble up through the water, and to race along beneath it: toads made noises like very young ducks, and advanced to the margin in twos and threes: overhead, bumblebees flew hither and thither in the thickening light, their drone coming and going like the sound of a gong. (*RN*, 192)

The 'life' evoked by the second sentence is a medley of noises and motions, under the water, along its surface and up in the air. Verbs proliferate, and the compound phrases – 'tadpoles and efts', 'twos and threes', 'hither and thither', 'coming and going' – enhance the general sense of overflowing energy.

Passages already analysed, from *Far from the Madding Crowd* and *Under the Greenwood Tree*, have shown how naturally Hardy associated movement in the heavens with the ceaseless movements on earth. The link can be quite casually implied, as in the account of the hill-top sentry duties of Corporal Tullidge and Simon Burden: 'Here they observed the nightly progress of the moon and stars, grew familiar with the heaving of moles, the dancing of rabbits on the hillocks, the distant hoot of owls, the bark of foxes from woods further inland...' (*T-M*, 214). Again the effect is to convey a sense that the human doings are all of a piece with the multifarious surrounding activities, terrestrial and celestial. Moon, stars, moles and rabbits are going about their business just as the sentries are.

Often Hardy shows a causative link between one kind of motion and another, as when weather-changes influence the huddling of sheep or the roosting of pheasants. Humans are by no means immune to such chain reactions. Stirred by the sight of a hawk chasing a duck 'Ethelberta impulsively started off in a rapid run that would have made a little dog bark with delight and run after...' (*HE*, 5).

Less obviously plants also participate in the general restlessness. Hardy's accounts of the energies of spring can verge on the melodramatic:

> The rush of sap in the veins of the trees could almost be heard. (*Wood*, 102)

> ...the rush of juices could almost be heard below the hiss of fertilization...(*Tess*, 151)

> ...that dull interval in a woodlander's life which coincides with great activity in the life of the woodland itself...when the saps are just beginning to heave with the force of hydraulic lifts inside all the trunks of the forest. (*Wood*, 185)

> The vegetable world begins to move and swell and the saps to rise, till...there are bustlings, strainings, united thrusts and pulls-altogether, in comparison with which the powerful tugs of cranes and pulleys in a noisy city are but pigmy efforts. (*FMC*, 127)

These are seasonal, and therefore exceptional, shows of collective might; but Hardy often dramatizes the encroaching strength of an individual plant:

> ...arms of ivy...were pushing in with such force at the eaves as to lift from their supports the shelves that were fixed there. (*Wood*, 20)

> ...the paving-stones were pushed sideways and upwards by the thrust of the grasses between them. (*DR*, 133)

Buildings are regularly depicted as being in effect under siege, subjected to such subterranean forces as the invasion of plants and insects as well as to the buffetings of rain and wind.

Hardy's responsiveness to movement, visible, covert or potential, in every aspect of nature, informs his poetry as well as his fiction. In 'Last Look round St Martin's Fair' there is a description of nightfall:

> The stars break out, and flicker in the breeze,
>   It seems, that twitches the trees. –
>   From its hot idol soon
> The fickle unresting earth has turned to a fresh patroon –
>   The cold, now brighter, moon.

It comes instinctively to Hardy to see our world as 'the fickle unresting earth'. 'A Sign-Seeker' implies that this instability is a necessary condition of life. Before lamenting his failure to detect any omens of an existence after death the speaker emphasizes his alertness both to natural manifestations –

> I have seen the lightning-blade, the leaping star,
>   The cauldrons of the sea in storm,
>   Have felt the earthquake's lifting arm ... –

and to human drama:

> I witness fellow earth-men surge and strive;
>   Assemblies meet, and throb, and part;
>   Death's sudden finger, sorrow's smart;
>   – All the vast various moils that mean a world alive.

Where there are no 'moils', the poet implies, there is death. The term recurs in a much later poem, 'According to the Mighty Working'. In the first stanza Hardy remarks that on a calm night, 'When moiling seems at cease ..., / We call the allurement Peace'. His second stanza, giving a retrospective emphasis to the word 'seems', claims that such a view is delusive:

> Peace, this hid riot, Change,
>   This revel of quick-cued mumming,
>   This never truly being,
>   This evermore becoming,

> This spinner's wheel onfleeing
> Outside perception's range.

An apprehension of constant ferment, alteration, provisionality, is fundamental to Hardy's view of life and to his art.

III

This imaginative tendency is carried to an extreme in *The Dynasts*, where the workings of the Immanent Will are dramatized in terms of movement. The Spirit of the Years contrives to display in visual terms (for the benefit of the Spirit of the Pities) the energies animating the people of war-torn Europe:

> You'll mark the twitchings of this Bonaparte
> As he with other figures foots his reel,
> Until he twitch him into his lonely grave:
> Also regard the frail ones that his flings
> Have made made gyrate like animalcula
> In tepid pools. (6)

In this panorama 'the peoples, distressed by events which they did not cause, are seen writhing, crawling, heaving, and vibrating in their various cities and nationalities'. When he exercises more fully his 'gift to visualise the Mode' the Spirit exhibits 'as one organism the anatomy of life and movement in all humanity and vitalized matter included in the display'.

This dramatization of the Will takes the descriptive habits exemplifed earlier in this chapter to a quasi-philosophical level unique to *The Dynasts* and therefore beyond the scope of this book. But the experiment does confirm, if confirmation is thought necessary, that Hardy's instinctive insistence, in his copious passages of description, on movement of all kinds, is a matter not of local observation merely, but of vision or diagnosis. He senses and implies an underlying *principle* of motion.

The Trumpet-Major, Hardy's novel about the Napoleonic wars, although written a quarter of a century before *The Dynasts*, shows a similar preoccupation with the collective: 'three or four thousand men of one machine-like movement' (14). When the troops parade on the Downs:

> The spectators...saw only troops and battalions in the concrete –
> straight lines of red, straight lines of blue, white lines formed of

innumerable knee-breeches, black lines formed of many gaiters, coming and going in kaleidoscopic change. (104)

A troop of marching soldiers is an obvious, perhaps too obvious, image of mass-activity, seeming automatism. As individuals, too, Hardy's main characters are repeatedly seen on the move. His tendency to begin a novel with a figure, or sometimes two figures, walking along a road has often been remarked upon. *Under the Greenwood Tree*, *The Woodlanders*, *The Mayor of Casterbridge*, *The Well-Beloved* and *Tess* are among the tales that start from description of isolated pedestrians.

In various ways, and for various reasons, the protagonists in Hardy's novels are shifted hither and thither, compelled by need or chance. *Tess* and *Jude*, in particular, are peripatetic in their very design, the main characters being unable to settle in any one place for long. Tess is repeatedly seen walking, from or towards Trantridge, Talbothays, Flintcomb-Ash, Emminster, Stonehenge. She also rides – in her father's wagon, in Alec's gig, on Alec's horse, in the milk-cart with Angel Clare. In either situation the journey is likely to be more than a physical one – she moves between states of mind. Walking or riding she is always 'driven'.

But it would be wrong to see Tess merely as a victim of external influences. Often what drives her is an inner force. Hardy's characters vary greatly in their power to decide their movements. The Loveday brothers join the army and the navy, respectively, and must go where they are posted. Stephen Smith is originally sent to Cornwall in the course of his employment. It is moral pressure, largely self-inflicted, that obliges Tess to go and seek out wealthy relatives: she feels she is responsible for the death of Prince and the consequent decline in the family fortunes. Still less autonomous are Little Time and his counterpart in 'Midnight on the Great Western', dispatched like parcels to destinations not of their choosing. At the other extreme Farfrae can leave his native Scotland, or Jude quit Marygreen for Christminster, very much of their own volition, driven only by self-generated pressures, by the desire to better themselves.

The potentialities and limitations of free will, however, are repeatedly interrogated by Hardy. In *A Pair of Blue Eyes* the heroine, Elfride, 'intensely *living* and full of movement' (30) seems to proclaim her independence in her instinctive mobility. Stephen sees her 'running with a boy's velocity, superadded to a girl's lightness, after a tame rabbit she was endeavouring to capture' (26). She proves to be a keen horsewoman, who gallops along the cliff-tops 'with flowing hair'. Later she frightens and angers Knight by daring to walk round the parapet of the church tower. Following the cliff rescue he watches her as 'She then ran off from him through the pelting rain like a hare; or more like a pheasant when, scampering away with a lowered tail, it has a mind to fly, but does not' (216). Yet this physical vigour belies a certain mental and emotional timidity. The abortive elopement with Stephen neatly sketches the temperament of a girl who 'has a mind to fly, but does not'. Vacillating as to whether to take the train to Plymouth for the crucial assignation she rides her horse first towards the station at St Launce's, then back towards home and then towards the station once more. 'Overwrought and trembling' she releases control of the reins 'and vowed she would be led whither the horse would take her' (109). She suspects that Pansy will go home for the sake of food, forgetting that the horse is often given a feed of corn at St Launce's – to which town, eventually, it therefore heads. Elfride is not interested in such explanations: 'All she cared to recognise was a dreamy fancy that today's rash action was not her own' (110). Her failure of commitment is immediately to be subjected to crueller scrutiny. It transpires, when she meets Stephen, that their marriage licence cannot be used in Plymouth, but only in London, where he obtained it. There is a London train about to depart: in response to his persuasions she enters it with him. By the time the pair reach Paddington, however, Elfride has changed her mind, and insists on returning to Cornwall forthwith:

> They run down the staircase – Elfride first – to the booking-office, and into a carriage with an official standing beside the door. 'Show your tickets, please.' They are locked in – men about the platform accelerate their velocities till they fly up and down like shuttles in a loom – a whistle – the waving of a flag – a human cry – a steam groan – and away they go to Plymouth again ... (113–14)

Elfride has made her decision, but caught up in the impersonal 'velocities' of the railway system she seems almost as helpless as Little Time or the Journeying Boy or many another Hardy character shifted mechanically 'like shuttles in a loom'.

Her 'wretched vacillation' is to be resumed. Even before they alight from the train at St Launce's she is saying 'firmly': ' "Stephen, once in London I ought to have married you ... " ' She renews her protestations of love – ' "Have I not shown beyond possibility of doubt that I can be nobody else's? Have I not irretrievably committed myself?" ' (117) – but for the reader, as possibly for Smith, they are less persuasive in the new context of her proved uncertainty.

This futile flurry of travelling is brought about by several factors. When Elfride leaves her future to chance the decisive factor proves to be a horse's eating habits. But then luck does play a part: things would have gone differently but for the mistake with the licence. Hardy also emphasizes that Stephen himself could have changed the course of events:

> Elfride had her sex's love of sheer force in a man, however ill-directed; and at that critical juncture in London Stephen's only chance of retaining the ascendancy over her that his face and not his parts had acquired for him, would have been by doing what, for one thing, he was too youthful to undertake – that was, dragging her by the wrist to the rails of some altar, and peremptorily marrying her. (125)

Earlier Hardy has referred to Smith's 'kindness' in letting Elfride return. Here the young man is made to sound weak. Perhaps both characteristics have been in play. An ironic comment on the expedition is the fact that on that same day Elfride's widowed father has quietly got himself remarried without a word to anyone. Such things can be done: we can, at least to some extent, take charge of our own doings.

It is an aspect of the parallelism of structure in this highly stylized novel that Elfride's fate is charted in a series of such journeys. Later she is to endure a second uncomfortable return trip from London – with Knight, and by sea. When she eventually accompanies both suitors on a third such journey it is again by train, and this time she is in her coffin.

In the elopement episode Elfride loses control of her own movements, as she is eventually to lose control of her own destiny. We are implicitly invited to wonder about the cause of her doing so. Is it external – bad luck, and Smith's failure of nerve? Or is it her own essential lack of confidence? Does her Character decide her Fate? In this case, as in countless such cases in Hardy, the answer is that Character and Fate are inseparable, obliged, like Nature and Nurture, to be awkward partners in a three-legged race. Whatever the characters hope or intend, that race will go on. Soon Smith will be heading for India.

Readers of *The Dynasts*, in particular, must wonder why Hardy shows so little interest in long-term political or economic patterns of motive. Since his habit of vision in this work involves seeing whole populations swayed by a common impulse it would seem natural for him to speculate, at least, as to whether that impulse might be social or revolutionary. But he does not do so. The prevailing impulse simply *is*. A possible explanation might be that Hardy sees political or economic 'movements' as merely specialized exemplifications of the Immanent Will, which is the ultimate impulse. Another is that he sees action of any kind as essentially irrational since it inevitably redefines itself in the very moment of performance. Elfride doesn't know exactly what she wants to do, or even exactly what she is about to do, till she finds herself doing it. In 'An August Midnight', as Hardy is writing about the visiting insects, 'My guests besmear my new-penned line'. Actions are modified before they are completed. Indeed they can all but lose contact with volition. Elfride's dilemma doesn't differ essentially from that of individuals far more famous. In *The Dynasts*, at the battle of Waterloo, the Immanent Will is again visualized: 'The web connecting all the apparently separate shapes includes WELLINGTON in its tissue with the rest, and shows him, like them, as acting while discovering his intention to act' (505).

IV

Hardy's characters are depicted as containers of energy. He tells of the 'unruly volcanic stuff beneath the rind of Michael Henchard' (*MC*, 113). Swancourt is first seen 'puffing and fizzing like a bursting bottle' (*PBE*, 8). Elfride, by contrast, has a 'weak' presence (7). Such inner force, or a lack of it, can be displayed in the way in which people move. Some, for example, have a distinctive habit of walking. Durbeyfield's legs are 'rickety, and there was a bias in his gait which inclined him somewhat to the left of a straight line' (13). The exhausted Mrs Yeobright walks with 'the jerk and limp of an invalid' (*RN*, 289). Henchard's measured springless walk', described on the first page of *The Mayor of Casterbridge*, marks him out as a skilled, rather than a general, country labourer, while the way he plants his feet suggests 'a dogged and cynical indifference, personal to himself'. His manner of walking is so intrinsic to his personality that there is a reprise of this description when the former Mayor eventually leaves Casterbridge, reverting to the status of labourer (313).

Hardy often shows mental or emotional states through physical manifestations. When Miss Aldclyffe is lost in concentrated thought she sits for some time immobilized, 'as if she were cast in bronze'. Then

> she moved and tapped her fingers upon the table at her side. Her pent-up ideas had finally found some channel to advance in.

Motions became more and more frequent as she laboured to carry further and further the problem which occupied her brain. She sat back and drew a long breath; she sat sideways and leant her forehead upon her arm. Later still she arose, walked up and down the room ... (*DR*, 130–1)

Frightened by Boldwood's threats of vengeance against Troy Bathsheba falls into 'distraction':

... instead of advancing further, she walked up and down, beating the air with her fingers, pressing her brow, and sobbing brokenly to herself. (*FMC*, 218)

Such episodes describe local eruptions of the physical energies and gestures through which Hardy regularly sets about defining character. The careful observation of exaggerated movement produces an odd and characteristic effect, somewhere between ethology and melodrama.

Elfride is a typical Hardy heroine in being characterized from the first by potential motion, by vibrancy or 'flexuousness' – a favourite word. When introducing Cytherea, in *Desperate Remedies*, he begins by drawing attention to her 'flexibility and elasticity':

Indeed, motion was her speciality, whether shown on its most extended scale of bodily progression, or minutely, as in the uplifting of her eyelids, the bending of her fingers, the pouting of her lip. The carriage of her head – motion within motion – a glide upon a glide – was as delicate as that of a magnetic needle. (44)

Unlike most Victorian heroines Hardy's leading ladies are physically active and enterprising. Captain De Stancy is instantly seduced by the sight of Paula Power working out in her private gymnasium, 'bending, wheeling, and undulating in the air' (*Lao*, 173). Jude finds his 'vibrant' cousin Sue revelatory: 'An exciting thought would make her walk ahead so fast that he could hardly keep up with her...' (104). Anne Garland breaks into a run as readily as Ethelberta or Elfride. Elizabeth-Jane Newson unexpectedly finds herself careering off at the first intimations of possible love between herself and Farfrae:

Without any consciousness of what she was doing she started running with all her might till she reached her father's door. 'O dear me – what am I at!' she thought as she pulled up, breathless. (111)

That Elizabeth-Jane, usually restrained in both speech and movement, should be surprised into this sudden sprint demonstrates that she has moved into the zone of romantic hyperactivity. For Hardy falling in love is likely to be signalized by extreme physical movement of some sort. Dick is first drawn close to Fancy in the excitement of the dance, where a whole household rocks with motion, watch-chains vibrate and ear-rings turn 'violent summersaults'. In the sword-play scene in *Far from the Madding Crowd* Bathsheba sees 'the hue of Troy's sword-arm, spread in a scarlet haze over the space covered by its motions, like a twanged harpstring' (195). Pierston first encounters, and falls in love with, Marcia amid fierce winds and 'a raking fusillade' of rain (*W-B*, 24). Knight's belated introduction to romantic love is imaged by the scene where he is hanging from a cliff-face with the 'boisterous tosses' of the sea far below his feet, and a fierce upward current of air lashing rain into his body.

These episodes, of course, and many others like them, are largely metaphorical in function, but they also serve to suggest that love is a site of turbulent activity. In that powerful magnetic field all is energy.

V

It might be useful at this stage to point up some inferences or connections latent in what has been said. Hardy seems to suggest that his human characters are subject to a life-force that animates everything in nature. Their motions, their activities, their journeyings, their feelings all express the workings of this force. They seek and are sought, move and are moved, act and are acted upon. There is no respite: the dance goes on.

But the process Hardy is concerned with is more complex than that summary suggests. The general emphases that have been described derive further power and interest from an elaborate substructure of incidental references which sustain and enhance them. Again *A Pair of Blue Eyes* offers a suggestive sequence of illustrations. As Elfride waits for her pony to make the decisive move her heart 'throbbed erratically'. During the return journey from Paddington with Smith she is 'wakeful and palpitating, hour after hour' (114). The same physical tremulousness is in evidence when she plays Knight at chess:

> The game progressed. Elfride's heart beat so violently that she could not sit still. Her dread was lest he should hear it. And he did

discover it at last – some flowers upon the table being set throbbing by its pulsations. (167)

Long after the game Elfride's pulse is still 'twanging like a harp-string, at the rate of nearly a hundred and fifty a minute' (168). It's hardly surprising that she shows a similar physical perturbation when Knight announces the news of their engagement to her former lover, Stephen Smith:

> Low as the words had been spoken, Elfride had heard them, and awaited Stephen's reply in breathless silence, if that could be called silence where Elfride's dress, at each throb of her heart, shook and indicated it like a pulse-glass, rustling also against the wall in reply to the same throbbing. (258)

Such instinctual motions – throbbings, palpitations, tremblings – are common in Hardy. Joan Grundy writes on this theme in *Hardy and the Sister Arts*, associating the pulsations with the rhythms of music and dance.[1] Her analysis is sensitive and wide-ranging, and I will be returning to it later in the chapter; but these manifestations can also be interpreted quasi-meteorologically. They stand for feeling – especially, though by no means exclusively, romantic and sexual feeling. Hardy's characters are swayed by internal gales, storms or shifts of temperature. He finds complex suggestion in laughter, in tears, even in yawning, sneezing, perspiring.

As there are winds without, so there can be winds within – most obviously evident in the form of sighs, or, as in *Tess*, the 'see-saw of … breath' (179). In an intimate moment with Edward Springrove Cytherea feels that 'His warm breath fanned and crept round her face like a caress' (*DR*, 76). There is a similarly erotic scene in *The Mayor of Casterbridge* when Farfrae gently blows husks off Elizabeth-Jane's clothing (95). Less romantically, as Oak draws off the wind from a 'blasted' sheep 'A current of air rushed up the tube forcible enough to have extinguished a candle held at the orifice' (*FMC*, 147). In a much more grisly episode, when Jude is obliged to slit the windpipe of his pig, the poor beast falls 'instantly silent, his dying breath coming through the hole' (64).

Hardy's awareness of internal tides is particularly evident in his numerous accounts of blushing. Since many of his characters are reticent or inarticulate it would be surprising if he did not make use of the occasional blush as an index of feeling. But the emphasis goes so far beyond such usage as to seem obsessive or systematic. In novel after novel blushes are repeatedly recorded: Elfride, for example, is shown blushing more than a score of times. Men redden as revealingly as women, if less frequently. While many such allusions are incidental – 'She could not help colouring at the confession ...' – Hardy often goes in for distinctive detail:

> Margery's face flushed up, and her neck and arms glowed in sympathy. ('Romantic Adventures of a Milkmaid', *Complete Stories*, 776)

> Her countenance changed. First she became crimson, and then the red subsided till it even partially left her lips. (*RN*, 286)

> De Stancy's bare military ears and closely cropped poll flushed hot. (*Lao*, 181)

> A flush covered her over, which seemed akin to a flush of rage. It was not exactly that, but she was excited. (*W-B*, 33)

> But she blushed fitfully, in her arms and hands as much as in her face. Not that she was overpowered by the great boots, formidable spurs, and other fierce appliances of his person, as he imagined; simply she had not been prepared to meet him there. (*T-M*, 52)

> In an instant Bathsheba's face coloured with the angry crimson of a Danby sunset. (*FMC*, 140)

> And while she looked the carmine flush with which warmth and sound sleep had suffused her cheeks and neck dissolved from view, and the death-like pallor in his face flew across into hers. (*RN*, 328)

> That minute's interval had brought the blood beating into her face, set her stinging as if aflame to the very hollows of her feet, and enlarged emotion to a compass which quite swamped thought. It had brought upon her a stroke resulting, as did that of Moses in Horeb, in a liquid stream – here a stream of tears. (*FMC*, 196–7)

It may not be a coincidence that Darwin showed a similar interest in the causes, the nature and the extent of blushing. In *The Expression of the Emotions in Man and Animals* (1872) he claims that 'Blushing is the most peculiar and the most human of all expressions. ... it would require an overwhelming amount of evidence to make us believe that any animal could blush.'[2] Strangely it is a reaction that cannot be elicited 'by any physical means'. He observes that the young blush more than the old, and women more than men, and that the blind are not immune. His comments on the extent of the area affected seem to justify Hardy's lavish descriptions:

> In most cases the face, ears and neck are the sole parts which redden; but many persons, whilst blushing intensely, feel that their whole bodies grow hot and tingle; and this shows that the entire surface must be in some manner affected.

He makes inquiries as to 'how far down the body blushes extend', and hears of a case where 'the chest, shoulders, arms, and whole body of a girl' are seen to redden. He notes that the pinkness may be succeeded by pallor, and that 'an intense blush is sometimes accompanied by a slight effusion of tears ...'

Given the extent of the shared interest and mutual endorsement implied in these quotations it comes as a surprise that Hardy and Darwin apparently differ on an essential issue. In *Far from the Madding Crowd* a ewe is shown to redden when left naked by the shearer:

> 'She blushes at the insult,' murmured Bathsheba, watching the pink flush which arose and overspread the neck and shoulders of the ewe where they were left bare by the clicking shears – a flush which was enviable, for its delicacy, by many queens of coteries, and would have been creditable, for its promptness, to any woman in the world. (152)

Shortly afterwards Boldwood appears, and Bathsheba herself becomes 'more or less red in the cheek, the blood wavering in uncertain flux and reflux over the sensitive space between ebb and flood' (154). The obvious implied comparison doesn't seem to be simply a matter of rhetoric or metaphor, since it confirms correspondences registered elsewhere. The most notable occurs in Oak's meeting with Fanny Robin:

> Gabriel's fingers alighted on the young woman's wrist. It was beating with a throb of tragic intensity. He had frequently felt the same quick hard beat in the femoral artery of his lambs when overdriven. (55–6)

The analogy has peculiar force here, since we have seen a flock of sheep driven to destruction and are later to see another lying 'blasted' in a field of clover. In this novel, as in others by Hardy, animals and

humans seem to be prey to the same physical, and perhaps even emotional, promptings: their blood is hurried by the same wants and fears.
If Fanny's blood can throb like that of an exhausted lamb a bashful
ewe can blush like Bathsheba. Similarly in *The Well-Beloved* we are told
that the impressionable Pierston, when in love, is 'inclined to palpitate
like a sheep in a fair' (*W-B*, 60).

VI

Hardy has several habitual ways of implying the position eventually
developed in *The Dynasts* – that motions of all kinds derive from a
common source. One such means, already tacitly illustrated within this
chapter, is metaphor. Repeatedly one species of movement is described
in terms of another. Stars flutter like birds, thrusting spring plants have
the power of cranes or pulleys, Elfride runs like a hare or pheasant, rain
is like seed, Bonaparte's victims are like animalcula. Here is a small
assortment of further examples:

> Anne's bosom began to surge and fall like a small tide ... (*T-M*, 338)

> ... his fingers tapping about upon the keys as mechanically as fowls
> pecking at barley-corns ... (*HE*, 27)

> ... said Henchard, in jerks, and moving like a great tree in a wind.
> (*MC*, 123)

> ... he had opened himself out like a sea-anemone ... (*W-B*, 91)

> ... the hissing fleece of froth slid again down the shingle, dragging
> the pebbles under it with a rattle as of a beast gnawing bones.
> (*HE*, 270)

> ... her hand trembled, the ardour of his affection being so palpable
> that she seemed to flinch under it like a plant in too burning a sun.
> (*Tess*, 173)

> ... the seeds of a neighbouring lime-tree ... flew out of the boughs
> downward like fledglings from their nest. (*Wood*, 160)

This is a sufficiently appropriate context in which to develop a comment from a previous chapter concerning Hardy's use of metaphor. His
early novels were much criticized on this score, his images being
described as 'strained and far-fetched', or 'far-fetched and unpleasant'.[3]
The recurrence of such complaints at least confirms how *noticeable* the

imagery is; he is undoubtedly unorthodox in this aspect of his writing. A Hardy metaphor is characteristically more than elucidatory or decorative: it equates. In relation to movement it can imply not merely that *A* has an incidental resemblance to *B*, but that the two entities are acted upon by the same forces, or are in effect doing the same thing. Through imagery Hardy projects a holistic sense of cross-relationship, of 'the anatomy of life and movement in all humanity and vitalized matter'.

This sense is further sustained by semantic recurrence. Certain verbs appear again and again, applied impartially to the movements of animals, birds, stars, seas, trees, insects, human beings. Many have to do with throbbing, pulsation, palpitation, quivering, vibration, twinkling, trembling, shivering. They may be used in a physical or a metaphorical sense, or may partake of both:

There, there, don't let that little heart beat itself to death: throb, throb, throb: it shakes the bed, you silly thing.' (*DR*, 117)

It is rarely that a man who can be entered and made to throb by the channel of his ears is not open to a similar attack through the channel of his eyes ... (*HE*, 17)

... the man whom Grace's matrimonial fidelity could not keep faithful was stung into passionate throbs of interest concerning her by her avowal of the contrary. (*Wood*, 249)

But let the elder be passed over here for those under whose bodices the life throbbed quick and warm. (*Tess*, 19)

... she found herself in the small room, quivering with emotion, a mist before her eyes and an excruciating pulsation in her brain ... (*FMC*, 307)

The air of the sleeping-chamber seemed to palpitate with the hopeless passion of the girls. (*Tess*, 149)

... the discovery sent a scarlet pulsation through her for the moment. (*Wood*, 210)

The words in question suggest biological rhythms. In several of the quoted extracts 'throb', in particular, has connotations both vascular and sexual, as in the poem 'I look into my glass'. The manipulation of such verbs to make them applicable to the beating of a heart, the flickering of light, the movement of waves, the gusting of wind, the flowing of blood or sap, implies the primacy of a single animating force in the universe, a force that for Hardy informs both animate and inanimate matter, and drives human beings from without and from within.

VII

Much has been written about the significance of dancing in Hardy's work. It would be surprising if this were not the case given its ubiquity and prominence. Certain obvious points need no more than brief reiteration here. Hardy loved dancing, and enjoyed writing about it, both in prose and in verse. He can represent it as the simple expression of spontaneous joy, as when Granfer Cantle, warmed by the bonfire to 'a cumulative cheerfulness, which soon amounted to delight', is moved 'to jig a private minuet', stick in hand (*RN*, 16). But he also finds dancing, in its social aspect, a useful narrative device. Like many another novelist he makes regular use of parties or other communal gatherings to bring his characters together and carry their relationships forward. In romantic and sexual terms dancing expedites the process:

> To dance with a man is to concentrate a twelvemonth's regulation fire upon him in the fraction of an hour. To pass to courtship without acquaintance, to pass to marriage without courtship, is a skipping of terms reserved for those alone who tread this royal road. (*RN*, 132)

It's in this context that Dick Dewy can make his first advances to Fancy Day. As 'They Dance More Wildly' the young couple, who hardly know one another, become 'practically one person'. Yet all this occurs in a defining social context: when the dancing is over Fancy need only don her hat and cloak to become 'altogether a different person … a woman somewhat reserved and of a phlegmatic temperament' (*UGT*, 60). Dick has to start again with his courtship proper. The Tranter's party is after all a relatively decorous affair. Things are very different at Chaseborough, where the dancers, 'overshoe in "scroff"', become 'a multiplicity of Pans whirling a multiplicity of Syrinxes', and the violently physical activity shades off into 'the ecstasy and the dream' (*Tess*, 66–7). Eustacia reaches these heights in a literal dream in which she is partnered by a man in silver armour: 'The mazes of the dance were ecstatic' (*RN*, 117). The dream is later to become a pseudo-reality not with Clym Yeobright, the subject of the fantasy, but with Wildeve at the East Egdon gipsying. The general atmosphere, as the dancers are 'spinning and fluctuating in the increasing moonlight', is propitious to passion:

> A whole village-full of emotion, scattered abroad all the year long, met here in a focus for an hour. The forty hearts of those waving couples were beating as they had not done since, twelve months before, they had come together in similar jollity. For the time Paganism was revived in their hearts, the pride of life was all in all, and they adored none other than themselves. (*RN*, 261–2)

In this bewildering and sensual context Eustacia is disorientated:

> The enchantment of the dance surprised her. A clear line of differ-ence divided like a tangible fence her experience within this maze of motion from her experience without it. (263)

The dance here is functioning in three ways. At the simplest level it provides an occasion to bring Eustacia and Wildeve into direct contact again. The propinquity, combined with the eroticism evoked by music and moonlight, reawakens their former sexual attraction. Beyond that, as often in Hardy, the dance becomes a metaphor for that very attrac-tion. The episode thus serves both narrative and thematic interests. In narrative terms the dance is an invaluable shorthand form, a brief and vivid alternative for what might otherwise have had to be a series of meetings and a gradual reawakening of desire. In thematic terms the description of the dance becomes an indirect description of the work-ings of sexual passion, of 'fascination', when 'the equilibrium of the senses' is disturbed, and the emotions are driven 'to rankness'.

Hardy often chooses to foreground the sexual aspect of the dance, as in 'The Fiddler of the Reels'. In contexts less hyperbolic the familiar verbs and metaphors discussed above can still point up such connota-tions. At Paula Power's ball 'The room was beating like a heart, and the pulse was regulated by the trembling strings of the most popular quadrille band in Wessex' (*Lao*, 220). The dance is charged with the sexual feeling that it will both express and exacerbate.

An early poem, 'The Dance at the Phoenix', suggests how complex are the pressures operating within and without. Jenny, once a light woman, but for many years a faithful wife, falls prey, at nearly sixty years of age, to unexpected temptation. Hearing that the regiment with which she once consorted, the King's-Own Cavalry, is back in town she cannot resist the temptation to attend their dance at the Phoenix Inn. A wild evening in which she has 'whirled', 'sped', 'soared and swooped' proves too much for her. She returns to the bed of her sleeping, unsuspecting husband, but is found dead the next morning. Hardy makes it sufficiently clear that Jenny's exploit is at least partly sexual in nature. It is 'with flushing fears' that she learns of the regiment's return. In the thick of the dance 'Jenny felt as in the days/Of her immodesty'. Returning to her husband she sheds tears:

> She felt she would give more than life
> To be the single-hearted wife
> That she had been erewhile...

But there has been a strong external stimulus in the form of the music. What sends 'springtime blood/...scouring through her like a flood' is the distant sound of the band, 'the throbbing "Soldier's Joy"'. Jenny makes for the ball 'with tune-led feet'. When she stands before the Inn it seems to her that the very stars are responding to the rhythms of the dance:

> ...over All-Saints', high and bright,
> Pulsed to the music Sirius white,
> The Wain by Bullstake Square.

The implication, of course, though it remains no more than a hint in this particular poem, is that Jenny, the music and the stars are expressing and responding to a universal energy. If 'The Dance at the Phoenix' is read with a literal eye Jenny must be counted distinctly unlucky in outdoing Car'line Aspent by actually contriving to dance herself to death. But of course the poem should not be so read. It is a folk-tale, or fable, which incidentally dramatizes one of Hardy's recurring themes: he shows, hyperbolically, how the energies that animate us, most obviously the sexual energies, are simultaneously burning us out. Even a star will pulse itself to extinction.

It would seem that in Hardy's terms dance is to movement as music is to sound. A natural and universal tendency has been subjected to human patterning. But in either case the question of ultimate autonomy remains. Is Man composer or mimic, choreographer or automaton? In *Tess of the d'Urbervilles* the description of the cavortings in the scroff at Chaseborough is prefaced by a reference to the 'dancing' of winged insects (66). In *The Hand of Ethelberta* Christopher Julian

1 *Landscape with Hagar and the Angel* by Claude Lorrain, 1646.

2 *The Leaping Horse* by John Constable R.A., *c.* 1824.

3 *The Cornfield* by John Constable R.A., 1826.

4 *Laughing Woman* (large version) by Medardo Rosso, 1891.

5 *Natura Morta* by Giorgio Morandi, 1963.

watches dancing couples 'whirl and turn ... knot themselves like house-flies and part again' (28). Once more an implicit question is posed: is the human revelry, after all, more purposeful or meaningful than that of insects?

The question has weight because Hardy sees dancing as the type of controlled human activity. After a detailed description of Tess's work as a harvester he goes on: 'The movements of the other women were more or less similar to Tess's, the whole bevy of them drawing together like dancers in a quadrille at the completion of a sheaf by each ...' (94). The metaphor is larger and looser when Marcia Bencomb returns to Pearston, in the first version of *The Well-Beloved*, feeling that her 'life's little measure is almost danced out' (256). In *The Dynasts* Napoleon's career is pictured in terms of him 'footing his reel' (6); at Waterloo the aides dart about 'like house-flies dancing their quadrilles' (489). The 'convergences' that feature so often in Hardy's work can be seen as the outcome of a deterministic choreography. They may well terminate in a literal collision, as when the *Titanic* hits an iceberg, or Farfrae's wagon is entangled with Henchard's, or Prince is killed. A year or two after this latter accident Tess herself is on a collision course with Angel Clare: '... they were converging, under an irresistible law, as surely as two streams in one vale' (133).

Hillis Miller, in *Thomas Hardy: Distance and Desire*, places the metaphor very perceptively. Having first made a general point – 'Each novel has ... a time special to it created by the slow dance of approach or withdrawal performed by the characters in their relations to one another' – he adds the rider: 'This country dance of approach and withdrawal is often symbolized by the literal dances which occur so frequently in Hardy's world ...'.[4] Joan Grundy has written illuminatingly on this theme. In the course of a densely illustrated argument she remarks: '... the dance of life as [Hardy] sees it occurs throughout all nature, "from the leaf on the tree to the titled lady at the ball"'.[5] The quotation is from the *Life*, and its immediate subject is 'the determination to enjoy'. Hardy likens it to 'pent-up water' which 'will find a chink of possibility somewhere'. The metaphors function in sequence. The inherent energy builds up till it escapes in motion which will shape itself into a 'dance' of some description.

Young lovers would probably prefer to be compared with converging streams rather than likened to house-flies, but the deterministic implication is as emphatic in either case. A first impression might well be that Hardy's fascination with movement is an expression of the fatalism often attributed to him. Men are merely 'figments', 'automata', predictably responding to predictable stimuli. Certainly there are passages in Hardy's fiction where he does seem to flirt briefly with a species of Naturalism. In *A Laodicean* Dare gives his susceptible father a stiff drink and then exposes him to the 'optical poem' of Paula Power at her gymnastic exercises. The effect is immediate, and Dare explains it to Havill in naturalistic terms: ' "A fermentation is beginning in him ... a purely chemical process; and when it is complete he will probably be clear, and fiery, and sparkling, and quite another man than the good, weak, easy fellow that he was"' (174). Dare is proved correct. The next chapter begins 'Captain De Stancy was a changed man', and recalls Dare's image in its final paragraph: 'The sky was lined with low cloud, within whose dense substance tempests were slowly fermenting for the coming days' (184). The suggestion, deliberate or accidental, is that sexual or emotional appetites function with the rough predictability of the weather.

In *A Pair of Blue Eyes*, when Elfride's love for Stephen Smith has met with angry disapproval from her father, Hardy begins a fresh section of a chapter in the following terms: 'Given an impulsive inconsequent girl, neglected as to her inner life by her only parent, and the following forces alive within her; to determine a resultant: ...' (105). There follows a separate paragraph listing the 'forces' concerned. The implication would seem to be that a defined situation involving defined forces will produce a predictable result. An authorial comment early in *Desperate Remedies* seems not dissimilar in spirit. The Graye children have been left orphaned and penniless:

> 'What will become of us now?' thought Owen continually.
>
> There is in us an unquenchable expectation, which at the gloomiest time persists in inferring that because we are *ourselves*, there must be a special future in store for us, though our nature and antecedents to the remotest particular have been common to thousands. Thus to Cytherea and Owen Graye the question how their lives would end seemed the deepest of possible enigmas. To others who knew their position equally well with themselves the question was the easiest that could be asked – 'Like those those of other people similarly circumstanced.' (49)

But the deterministic, or naturalistic, suggestion is not sustained in the event. The Grayes move into a spectacularly 'special future'. Elfride's progress, as has been shown, is similarly unpredictable. Whoever or whatever the choreographer, the scenes can vary: the performers have at least some small degree of autonomy, and there is always 'the persistence of the unforeseen'. It is only the conclusion of the ball that is unconditionally determined.

VIII

What makes Hardy's concern with movement worth writing about is also what makes it hard to write about. The theme is omnipresent. Illustration needs to be copious and varied enough to make that point, but must also stop short of tedious repetitiveness. Perhaps one last litany from a single work will serve to enforce the density and diversity of such emphases. In *The Woodlanders* the reader is invited to see or hear 'lips moving and heads nodding in animated private converse', branches 'rubbing each other into wounds', sparrows walking, 'the regular dripping of the fog', birds tumbling into a fire, hares and rabbits bounding, smoke creeping away through bushes, leaves unrolling in the spring or resuming shape after the pressure of footsteps, carriages colliding. We are told of ivy pushing its way inside a house, of 'the whitey-brown' creeping out of the earth, of the rush of sap, of women being 'carried about like corks upon the waves of masculine desires', of 'the regular terrestrial roll that produced the season's changes', of the 'infinitesimal movement of muscle, curve, hair and wrinkle' from which 'moods and meanings' can be deduced.

Wherever Hardy turns his gaze the thing seen tends to lapse into disequilibrium, uncertainty, variation, flux. Everything in his landscapes is unstable, and the Figures partake of the instability – which becomes an essential element of the story to be told. The lives he writes about are mutable and unpredictable not merely just as, but *because*, nature at large is mutable and unpredictable, boisterous with movement, struggle, defeat, realignment.

'Motion', a favourite Hardy word, was, of course, a key concept for Wordsworth, and one can sense behind many of Hardy's descriptions the account of the abstract 'something' in 'Tintern Abbey':

> A motion and a spirit, that impels
> All thinking things, all objects of all thought,
> And rolls through all things.

But the stronger emphasis is undoubtedly Darwinian. The 'thinking things' have a status no more significant than that of the 'objects of all thought' and are alike caught up in the endless movement which tends towards dissolution.

5
Erosion, Deformation and Reformation

Hardy repeatedly draws attention to tracks, prints and other such tokens. George Somerset, in *A Laodicean*, guesses from marks in the snow that a letter has been delivered to him: 'he could trace the post-man's footmarks as he entered over the bridge, knowing them by the dot of his walking-stick' (264). In an earlier scene in the same novel the entrance to the barracks is recognizable through 'wheel-tracks and a regular chain of hoofmarks left by the departed batteries ... imprinted in the gravel between the open gates' (146). *The Trumpet-Major* mentions a more complex 'geological record': 'The dry hard mud of the opening was marked with several horse and cow tracks, that had been half obliterated by fifty score sheep tracks, surcharged with the tracks of a man and a dog' (46). When Gabriel Oak and Jan Coggan are on the trail of a horse apparently stolen they follow, and strive to inter-pret, a series of shifting traces. The World Classics edition of *Far from the Madding Crowd* has happily restored Hardy's manuscript sketches, not published in his own lifetime. This expanded account shows a visual punctiliousness appropriate to a story much concerned with the close reading of signs: 'The footprints forming this recent impression were full of information as to pace: being difficult to describe in words they are given in the following diagram ... ' (221). In fact there is a sequence of such diagrams, showing successively that the horse is galloping, cantering, trotting, walking and eventually lamed.

This interest in tracks is all of a piece with Hardy's emphasis on motion. Life is movement, movement leaves traces, and those traces are there to be read as evidence of what has been going on around us. The landscape is alive with meanings. The cases quoted above all con-cern 'recent impressions', records of activity which has barely preceded the narrative present. They function simply as circumstantial clues. But often impressions of this kind have a different status, as the last faint mementoes of lost happiness or lost love. Hardy can underline the point by giving them a slightly extended life. In *Far from the Madding Crowd* Boldwood, looking out on a frozen landscape after a night spent brooding on Bathsheba's valentine, sees 'the footprints of a few birds ... frozen to a short permanency' (104). There are many instances in Hardy's work of such evanescent marks being temporarily preserved. Melbury covers up a footprint made by his daughter Grace just before her departure for college, and regularly goes to look at this valedictory sign. For Hardy the poet a circle of burnt sticks marks the place 'Where the Picnic Was'. 'Four Footprints' record the final parting of two lovers:

> Here are the tracks upon the sand
> Where stood last evening she and I –
> Pressed heart to heart and hand to hand;
> The morning sun has baked them dry.

A comparable, but much more elaborate, set of impressions features to quizzical effect in *A Pair of Blue Eyes*. Elfride notices, in the rectory garden, alongside a hedge, 'a little footpath, the distinctive and altogether exceptional feature of which consisted in its being only about ten yards long; it terminated abruptly at each end' (*PBE*, 107). She realizes that this 'sentry path' must have been trodden by her father. Then she looks beyond, to the other side of the hedge:

> Here was another sentry path. It was like the first in length, and began and ended exactly opposite the beginning and ending of its neighbour, but it was thinner and less distinct.
> Two reasons existed for the difference. This one might have been trodden by a similar weight of tread to the other, exercised a less number of times; or it might have been walked just as frequently, but by lighter feet.
> Probably a gentleman from Scotland Yard, had he been passing at the time, might have considered the latter alternative as the more probable. (107)

It later emerges that the twin paths are the record of the courtship of her father and Mrs Troyton, idiosyncratically pursued by means of parallel pacings either side of the privet hedge. The middle-aged lovers have trodden out the little equals sign on the way to their marriage of convenience, which takes place at the very time when Elfride's youthful passions have sent her flying fruitlessly to London and back. This hieroglyph is teasingly mysterious: like the night-noises heard by Cytherea it demands an explanation. It is also particularly Hardyesque in its ambiguity, hovering between the wry and the sardonic. The parallel lines that cannot meet would seem to stand for the detached, circumscribed relationship of the elderly lovers, but they could also represent the unfulfilled love of Stephen and Elfride. On a cynical reading they might suggest the delusiveness of romantic love in general.

The slightly extended preservation of such signs does not significantly modify their transience. Rather, the effect is to dramatize it. These are almost the faintest of ripples on the surface of time. They allow a moment of contemplation, a chance to glimpse evanescence at work. People move on and are forgotten; their brief traces are pitiful and meaningful in their very brevity. Hardy observes in the *Life*:

> '... An object or mark raised or made by man on a scene is worth ten times any such formed by unconscious Nature. Hence clouds, mists, and mountains are unimportant beside the wear on a threshold, or the print of a hand.' (120)

For obvious reasons it is often the domestic setting that displays such hints of wear and tear. In *Far from the Madding Crowd* Hardy describes Gabriel Oak's 'old furniture' with a phrase borrowed from his friend William Barnes:

> all a-sheenen
> Wi' long years o' handlen. (406)

Similarly an inn-door is seen to be 'shiny and paintless from the rub of infinite hands and shoulders' (*MC*, 256). This adjective 'shiny', and variants of it, are common in Hardy's writings as indicating a kind of glaze wrought by the polishing process of year upon year of intimate handling. 'Old Furniture' explains the habit of vision that lies behind the recurrence of such terms:

> I know not how it may be with others
>   Who sit amid relics of householdry
> That date from the days of their mothers' mothers,
>   But well I know how it is with me
>   Continually.

I see the hands of the generations
That owned each shiny familiar thing
In play on its knobs and indentations,
And with its ancient fashioning
Still dallying…

Here the 'shininess' is testimony to multiple ownership stretching far back into the past. The wear on the objects precipitates memories. In *The Mayor of Casterbridge* there is a description of this kind which Hardy presumably valued, since he had already included it in his essay 'The Dorsetshire Labourer'. It depicts an old shepherd at a hiring-fair:

He was now so bowed by hard work and years that, approaching from behind, a person could hardly see his head. He had planted the stem of his crook in the gutter and was resting upon the bow, which was polished to silver brightness by the long friction of his hands. He had quite forgotten where he was, and what he had come for, his eyes being bent on the ground. (161)

The old man's life has subsided to a virtual nullity, barely present even to himself. Only the bow of his crook offers, in its worn brightness, a memorial to the many years of toil. Similarly the floor of the barn in *Far from the Madding Crowd*, is described as 'polished by the beating of flails for many generations' (151), while the wooden posts in the cow-shed at Talbothays have been 'rubbed to a glassy smoothness by the flanks of infinite cows and calves of bygone years' (111). The daily friction of human and animal activity has left a minimal mark on the surface of things – buffing them to a gloss, a shininess, which tells us that life has been here.

Hardy can feel affection for traces less dignified than this. He describes thumb-stained playing-cards (*Wood*, 58), the 'torn, kicked and scraped' baize lining of an old church pew (*Lao*, 112), Durbeyfield's hat, with a patch 'quite worn away at its brim where his thumb came in taking it off' (*Tess*, 13) or Bible pages 'quite worn away at much-read verses by the forefingers of unpractised readers in former days' (*FMC*, 98).

Hardy's emphasis here might seem so Wordsworthian as even to be directly traceable to the earlier poet. Wordsworth's Wanderer is moved by the discovery, near Margaret's ruined cottage, of

The useless fragment of a wooden bowl,
Green with the moss of years, and subject only

To the soft handling of the elements...
('The Excursion', Book I, 493ff.)

He sees it, presumably, as an aspect of

That secret spirit of humanity
Which, 'mid the calm oblivious tendencies
Of nature, 'mid her plants, and weeds, and flowers,
And silent overgrowings, still survived.
(Ibid., 927ff.)

There are many relics of this sort in Wordsworth's verse: the unfinished sheepfold left by Michael, an abandoned pile of turf, a shepherd's crook lodged for years on a crag after its owner has fallen to his death.

Hardy, of course, deals in just such relics: the drinking glass trapped 'Under the Waterfall', the bird-cage which Elizabeth-Jane discovers after her wedding, the worm-eaten pikes and other local tokens of the Napoleonic period, described in the Preface to *The Trumpet-Major*. But in several important respects his vision differs from Wordsworth's. For Hardy the process of erosion that will eventually dissolve all man-made objects is not merely an effect of Nature, and does not begin with the death of the owner. All living things and all inanimate ones are locked into an unending system of mutual attrition.

II

The point is made most often, and most obviously, in relation to buildings, repeatedly depicted by Hardy as he depicts the Christminster colleges in *Jude the Obscure:* 'wounded, broken, sloughing off their outer shape in the deadly struggle against years, weather, and man' (84). Hardy shows time – 'the years O!' – effacing stone, bricks and mortar as it effaces lives. Even a structure as basic as 'a Druidical trilithon' can display its scars: 'Each stone had been worn, scratched, washed, nibbled, split, and otherwise attacked by ten thousand different weathers...' ('What the Shepherd Saw', *Complete Stories*, 656). Buildings are shown to age much as human beings do. In *Desperate Remedies* the Three Tranters, an old coaching inn, is seen in its dotage: 'the line of roofs – once so straight – over the decayed stalls, had sunk into vast hollows till they seemed like the cheeks of toothless age' (153). A comparable fate is befalling the Buck's Head, in 'The Waiting Supper': 'the stable-roofs were hollow-backed, the landlord was asthmatic…' (*Complete Stories*, 570). In 'The Two Houses' the 'smart newcomer' points out to his veteran neighbour that he is:

> …haler than you with your cracked old hide,
> Loose casements, wormy beams, and doors that jam.

But time is, after all, a passive element in the process of attrition. It is not time, but motion of various kinds that gradually undermines physical substance: the movements of wind and weather, people, insects and animals. Man and the elements unconsciously collaborate to destroy, as in the case of the bridges at the lower end of Casterbridge: 'Every projection in each was worn down to obtuseness, partly by weather, more by friction from generations of loungers, whose toes and heels had from year to year made restless movements against these parapets…' (*MC*, 223).

It is weather that does the dramatic damage. The destruction can be peremptory: in *Two on a Tower* the great winds which lift the dome off Swithin's observatory blow down the chimney and part of the upper floor of his grandmother's cottage. More generally the moaning winds, the driving rain, so often heard in Hardy's fiction, scour and sap and subvert. Stone, wood, glass, plaster, even iron, are all at the mercy of the elements:

> …every corner of every stone was completely rounded off by the waves of wind and storm. (*HE*, 149)

> It was one of those nights when cracks in the walls of old churches widen, when ancient stains on the ceilings of decayed manor-houses are renewed and enlarged… (*RN*, 362).

> The walls, built of kneaded clay originally faced with a trowel, had been worn by years of rain-washings to a lumpy, crumbling surface, channelled and sunken from its plane… (*MC*, 331).

Lower down the scale of depredation people are shown to wear out the houses they inhabit. Thresholds have been abraded by the passing of countless boots and shoes. Christopher Julian, when visiting Ethelberta's house in London 'stole a glimpse at the door and at the steps, imagined what a trifle of the depression worn in each step her feet had tended to produce, and strolled home again' (*HE*, 63). The floor of Hardy's childhood home has been left 'Footworn and hollowed and thin' by generations of living, working and dancing ('The

Self-Unseeing'). When Grace visits Giles's hut she finds that 'the natural sandstone floor was worn into hills and dales by long treading, so that none of the furniture stood level, and the table slanted like a desk' (*Wood*, 225). At Warren's Malthouse 'The stone-flag floor was worn into a path from the doorway to the kiln, and into undulations everywhere' (*FMC*, 57). During a visit to Venice Hardy observes of St Mark's: 'That floor, of every colour and rich device, is worn into undulations by the infinite multitudes of feet that have trodden it, and *what* feet there have been among the rest!' (*Life*, 201).

In his observations and meditations on this theme Hardy shows himself a positive connoisseur, in a curious way seeming to savour the processes and nuances of decay. Visitors to Lincoln's Inn Fields in August find that 'rust was the only active agent to be seen there':

> The palings along the front were rusted away at their base to the thinness of wires, and the successive coats of paint, with which they were overlaid in bygone days, had been completely undermined by the same insidious canker, which lifted off the paint in flakes, leaving the raw surface of the iron on the palings, standards, and gate hinges, of a staring blood-red. (*DR*, 136)

The houses at the centre of Hardy's novels usually show their age in various of the ways outlined above. Stancy Castle, home of Paula Power in *A Laodicean*, is 'Irregular, dilapidated, and muffled in creepers' (22). Only one wing is still inhabited. Overcombe Mill, in *The Trumpet-Major*, has 'two zigzag cracks in the wall' and at one end presents 'the appearance of a hard-worked house slipping into the river' (16). High-Place Hall, Lucetta's Casterbridge residence, has 'birds'-nests in its chimneys, damp nooks where fungi grew, and irregularities of surface direct from Nature's trowel' (140). A mask on an outside arch has been damaged by generations of stone-throwing boys, whose efforts have 'chipped off the lips and jaws as if they had been eaten away by disease' (142). In his sonnet 'Rome: Building a New Street in the Ancient Quarter' Hardy meditates on the mortality of masonry:

> And cracking frieze and rotten metope
> Express, as though they were an open tome
> Top-lined with caustic monitory gnome;
> 'Dunces, Learn here to spell Humanity!'
> And yet within these ruins' very shade

The singing workmen shape and set and join
Their frail new mansion's stuccoed cove and quoin
With no apparent sense that years abrade,
Though each rent wall their feeble works invade
Once shamed all such in power of pier and groin.

The vulnerability of stone is also demonstrated by a number of the statues and effigies described by Hardy. In 'The Children and Sir Nameless' the negatively eponymous knight, an autocrat, bully and child-hater, proclaims:

'To be perpetuate for my mightiness
Sculpture must image me when I am gone.'

An outsize alabaster figure is duly carved, but years later, when the family of this village Ozymandias has died out, it is moved to the floor of the church, below the seats for the schoolchildren:

And they
Kicked out his name, and hobnailed off his nose;
And, as they yawn through sermon-time, they say,
'Who was this old stone man beneath our toes?'

Stancy Castle is one of a number of buildings in Hardy's fiction which are eventually destroyed altogether. Like the Three Tranters inn it is burned down. In *A Pair of Blue Eyes* Elfride makes the mistake of remarking 'in winning tones' to Knight ' "Thou hast been my hope, and a strong tower for me against the enemy" ' (304). Within minutes the church tower that the lovers have been looking at collapses, killing the ill-fated Mrs Jethway. Giles Winterborne's fortunes reach their lowest ebb when his cottage is demolished. Conversely it is in the prosperity of old age that Jocelyn Pierston buys some damp Elizabethan cottages in order to pull them down and erect replacements 'with hollow walls, and full of ventilators' (*W-B*, 205). In *The Mayor of Casterbridge* a description of the ostensibly fictitious Casterbridge High Street carries a footnote: 'Most of these old houses have now been pulled down (1912)' (30). The village of Marygreen, in *Jude the Obscure*, has been partly destroyed even before the story begins:

Many of the thatched and dormered dwelling-houses had been pulled down of late years, and many trees felled on the green. Above all the original church, hump-backed, wood-turreted, and quaintly hipped, had been taken down and either cracked up into heaps of road-metal in the lane, or utilized as pig-sty walls, garden seats, guard-stones in fences, and rockeries in the flower-beds of the neighbourhood. (6)

The cottage inhabited by Wordsworth's Margaret is seen as stable enough during her happy married life. Michael's cottage is actually a beacon – called locally 'the Evening Star'. Only when their owners leave or pass on, and the buildings are handed over to the elements, do time and nature begin to encroach. By contrast Hardy's characters live in a visibly changing landscape. The very fabric of their houses and churches is decaying and collapsing around them. Almost parodically extreme is the case of Oxwell Hall in *The Trumpet-Major*:

Mustard and cress could have been raised on the inner plaster of the dewy walls at any height not exceeding three feet from the floor; and mushrooms of the most refined and thin-stemmed kinds grew up through the chinks of the larder paving. As for the outside, Nature, in the ample time that had been given her, had so mingled her filings and effacements with the marks of human wear and tear upon the house that it was often hard to say in which of the two, or if in both, any particular obliteration had its origin. The keenness was gone from the mouldings of the doorways, but whether worn out by the rubbing past of innumerable people's shoulders, and the moving of their heavy furniture, or by Time in a grander and more abstract form, did not appear. The iron stanchions inside the window-panes were eaten away to the size of wires at the bottom where they entered the stone, the condensed breathings of generations having settled there in pools and rusted them. The panes themselves had either lost their shine altogether, or become iridescent as a peacock's tail. (47)

This is erosion at its most full-blooded. Stonework, plaster, iron and glass have all suffered. A combination of forces has wrought the damage: decay, rising damp, plant life, the elements without, the inhabitants within. The movements and even the breathings of the occupants have helped to wear out the fabric. Outside there are animals assisting in the process: 'some heifers were amusing themselves by stretching up their necks and licking the mouldings of any salient stonework' (48).

Many such a description in Hardy is sombre in tone, but this particular passage has an undeniable relish about it. There is amusement, even a touch of exhilaration, at the sense that all these forces are zestfully busying themselves about the place. 'How interesting it all is', suggests the author's tone. How curious that decay should produce, as a by-product, a peacock-like iridescence. How ironic the gap between the depredations of Time in its 'grander and more abstract form' and the lickings of cattle. The hint of amusement remains present in the description of the Hall's appropriately dilapidated proprietor. He is in the same plight as the landlord of the Buck's Head, ageing along with his building, like a captain ready to go down with his ship. What is first seen of him, through a crack in the door, is 'a strip of decayed face, including the eye and some forehead wrinkles' (48). Later we learn that 'The edge of his skull round his eye-sockets was visible through the skin, and he had a mouth whose corners made towards the back of his head on the slightest provocation'. Dissolution, it would seem, can have its grimly comic aspect.

At the opposite extreme, in terms of seriousness of tone and inference, is the episode in *Desperate Remedies* when Cytherea and Manston are together in Carriford church:

> Everything in the place was the embodiment of decay: the fading red glare from the setting sun, which came in at the west window, emphasizing the end of the day and all its cheerful doings, the mildewed walls, the uneven paving stones, the wormy pews, the sense of recent occupation, and the dank air of death which had gathered with the evening, would have made grave a lighter mood than was Cytherea's then. (257)

The atmosphere has its effect on both characters. Manston proves as susceptible to the lifelessness of the rotting building as he was earlier to the vitality of the ephemerons in the water-butt. He claims that he considers himself 'called upon to be honest, from very despair of achieving anything by stratagem in a world where the materials are such as these'. Cytherea replies that she feels 'almost ashamed to be seen walking such a world'. While she is in this low mood Manston proposes to her, not for the first time, and she is moved to accept.

The episode clearly derives from the poem 'Her Dilemma', where a rather different personal drama is given a similar setting:

> The two were silent in a sunless church,
> Whose mildewed walls, uneven paving-stones,
> And wasted carvings passed antique research;
> And nothing broke the clock's dull monotones.

Leaning against a wormy poppy-head,
So wan and worn that he could scarcely stand,
– For he was soon to die, – he softly said,
'Tell me you love me!' – holding long her hand.

She would have given a world to breathe 'yes' truly,
So much his life seemed hanging on her mind,
And hence she lied, her heart persuaded throughly
'Twas worth her soul to be a moment kind.

But the sad need thereof, his nearing death,
So mocked humanity that she shamed to prize
A world conditioned thus, or care for breath
Where Nature such dilemmas could devise.

Hardy's attachment to this early poem seems clearly demonstrated in his willingness to rewrite it for the rather different context in *Desperate Remedies*. Poem and passage, taken together, shed light on one of the ways in which he relates Figures to Background. Cytherea, whose reaction is so similar to that of the girl in the poem, has, like her, a 'dilemma'. The implication, in either case, is that the dilemma is to a significant extent defined, or re-defined, by the context. The mildewed walls, the worn stone, the worm-eaten woodwork at the same time amplify and simplify the predicament. They serve as reminders that Life is put together from wretchedly perishable materials. Nothing lasts. We all die, if at different speeds. There are no certitudes or absolutes. Our best course of action can be no more than makeshift moral pragmatism.

III

Hardy shows vegetable and animal agents impartially speeding up the progress of decay in buildings of all kinds. Worms infiltrate church woodwork; mice invade Stancy Castle. In 'The House of Hospitalities' Hardy sees worm, mole and spider at work in the friendly cottage where he was brought up. Such activities could in theory be interpreted as manifestations of 'the calm oblivious tendencies of nature' described by Wordsworth. But this is not the point which Hardy chooses to make. He does not contrast the ephemeral works and doings of man with the continuities of nature. Nature is shown to be not merely destructive but self-destructive, endlessly wearing itself out. Certainly Man does his share, snaring rabbits, shooting birds, starving horses, killing pigs, but left to themselves animals will prey upon one another. Hardy makes incidental allusion to 'a solitary thrush cracking a small snail upon the doorstone' (*RN*, 328), or to 'Owls that had been catching mice in the outhouses, rabbits that had been eating the winter-greens in the gardens, and stoats that had been sucking the blood of the rabbits...' (*Wood*, 19). Sue Bridehead might be lamenting on Hardy's behalf when she exclaims 'O why should Nature's law be mutual butchery!' (*Jude*, 323).

Many of these comments, of course, are refractions of Darwin. *On the Origin of Species* remarks:

> We behold the face of nature bright with gladness, we often see super-abundance of food; we do not see, or we forget, that the birds which are idly singing round us mostly live on insects or seeds, and are thus constantly destroying life; or we forget how largely these songsters, or their eggs, or their nestlings, are destroyed by birds and beasts of prey; we do not always bear in mind, that though food may be now superabundant, it is not so at all seasons of each recurring year.[1]

Hardy repeatedly echoes this negative emphasis on destruction. Only rarely does he assert the Darwinian case that such tendencies may alternatively be regarded as salutary and progressive.

Even plants are shown locked into conflict: 'trees close together, wrestling for existence, their branches disfigured with wounds resulting from their mutual rubbings and blows' (*Wood*, 234). Henchard's garden is described as 'silent, dewy, and full of perfume', but at the back of it 'the long-tied espaliers, as old as the old house itself, had grown so stout, and cramped, and gnarled that they had pulled their stakes out of the ground, and stood distorted and writhing in vegetable agony, like leafy Laocoons' (*MC*, 76–7). The poem 'In a Wood' takes the civil strife of trees as its theme. The narrator retires to the woodland, 'City-opprest', seeking in Nature 'a soft release/From men's unrest':

> But, having entered in,
>   Great growths and small
> Show them to men akin –
>   Combatants all!
> Sycamore shoulders oak,
> Bines the slim sapling yoke,
> Ivy-spun halters choke
>   Elms stout and tall.

Depressed by this vegetable hostility and destructiveness he turns back to his own kind, whose conflicts are at least mitigated by friendliness, conversation and – sometimes – 'Life-loyalties'.

'In a Wood' carries the note See *'The Woodlanders'*. The hint underlines the inference, plain enough in its title and text, that the novel develops a systematic comparison between the blind battlings for survival of the plants and the conflicts of the human characters. Parallelism often moves towards symbiosis. The local timber-dealers affect eccentric walking-sticks, exhibiting 'various monstrosities of vegetation, the chief being corkscrew shapes in black and white thorn, brought to that pattern by the slow torture of an encircling woodbine during their growth, as the Chinese have been said to mould human beings into grotesque toys by continued compression in infancy' (41). There is complex inter-involvement between the human and the arboreal struggles. John South feels mortally oppressed by the tall elm outside his cottage, which was 'quite a small tree' when he was a little boy but now looks capable of crushing his home: 'There he stands, threatening my life every minute that the wind do blow.' It is 'the sight of its motion, and sound of its sighs' (70) that has inspired the fear. To limit these manifestations Giles 'shrouds' the tree, hacking off branch after branch, but the only effect is to make it seem 'taller than ever'. As a desperate last measure the elm is felled – but its sudden disappearance gives South a fatal shock. The men kill the tree and the tree kills the man within the space of twenty-four hours.

It is while Giles is in the process of shrouding the elm that Grace calls up to him from below and announces, in effect, that they can never be married. Giles responds 'in an enfeebled voice' that he has nothing to say. Much later, however, when he descends, 'the tree seemed to shiver, then to heave a sigh' (73). It sighs both for its own wounds and for those of the wood-cutter. Tree and man have suffered in parallel.

A number of Hardy's poems develop similar themes. In 'Logs on the Hearth' and 'The Felled Elm and She' a tree is seen as a record of a parallel human life, a calendar in vegetable form. 'The Ivy-Wife', speaking in the first person, relates how her loving embrace, resisted by beech and plane, is eventually accepted by an ash. Strangled by her encroachments it dies, destroying her, too, in its fall. So neatly poised is the poem that one cannot say whether the implied human story is substance or metaphor. In a sense it doesn't matter. In either case the same process is enacted, and for the same reasons. Men and trees destroy themselves and one another in similar ways.

IV

It was suggested above that for Hardy attrition is a reciprocal process: as his characters leave their small marks on their environment, so that environment leaves its mark on them. People wear out more quickly than things. A stone threshold may bear the tokens of centuries of use, but the 'ephemeral human carcase' (*RN*, 139) can be consumed at an alarming rate. Squire Derriman's case is not the most extreme: many a Hardy character is physically damaged. Edmond Willowes, of 'Barbara of the House of Grebe', suffers Gothic mutilations in a fire – ' "Neither nose nor ears, nor lips scarcely!" ' (*Collected Stories*, 249). Cripplestraw, in *The Trumpet-Major*, has had a silver plate let into his head as a result of injuries suffered at Valenciennes. Bob Loveday returns from the wars with a 'chasm' in his skull caused by a cutlass blow. Fancy Day's father has had his nose knocked back in a fight, 'so that when the sun was low and shining in his face people could see far into his head' (*UGT*, 95). Marty South's hair is cut off to adorn another woman. When her father dies his brain is somehow confiscated for Fitzpiers's investigative purposes.

These are special cases, hyperbolical encroachments, but life's normal processes of attrition are shown to be damaging enough. Hardy observes of the scholars in the British Museum Reading Room: 'Dissolution is gnawing at them all' (*Life*, 215). Women, in particular, have all too short a prime. Lucetta Templeman and Felice Charmond, attractive women in their twenties, already have a sense that their charms are fading. Both are described by a favourite Hardy phrase: 'a little worn'. Viviette Constantine, in her early thirties, is 'worn and faded' and speaks of herself as 'an old woman'. To read widely in Hardy is to become aware of his obsession with 'Wives in the Sere' or 'The Faded Face'. The 'aged child', Little Time, protests dispiritingly to Jude and Sue: 'I should like the flowers very, very much, if I didn't keep on thinking they'd be all withered in a few days!' (312). The headlong celerity with which Hardy's heroines age tempts the thought that he might reasonably have conceded 'Little Time, c'est moi'.

It's not uncommon for his characters to be re-encountered – as is Viviette – after an interval of some years. Invariably the passage of time has greatly altered their features. When Susan Henchard reappears 'her face ha(s) lost much of its rotundity; her skin ha(s) undergone a textural change' and her hair is 'considerably thinner than heretofore' (*MC*, 21). Nicholas Long, in 'The Waiting Supper', has similarly deteriorated in the course of an absence of fifteen years: 'He was still barely of middle age, but it could be seen that a haze of gray was settling upon the locks of his hair, and that his face had lost colour and curve...' (*Collected Stories*, 570). In a diary note dated March 28, 1888, Hardy remarks: 'On returning to London after an absence I find the people of my acquaintance abraded, their hair disappearing; also their flesh, by degrees' (*Life*, 215). Worse things happen in the poems. The narrator of 'The Revisitation', who meets a former lover again after twenty years, has a particularly disagreeable surprise as 'her image then I scanned':

> That which Time's transforming chisel
> Had been tooling night and day for twenty years, and tooled
>   too well,
> In its rendering of crease where curve was, where was
>   raven, grizzle –
> Pits, where peonies once did dwell.

'In the Night She Came' tells the same story proleptically. A lover rashly boasts to his mistress that time will never change his feelings. That night she appears to him, in a dream or in his imaginings:

> Toothless, and wan, and old,
> With leaden concaves round her eyes,
> And wrinkles manifold.

Recalling his boast he plaintively protests; 'Well...I did not think/You would test me quite so soon!' It's hardly surprising that the real-life relationship suffers:

> ...when next day I paid
> My due caress, we seemed to be
> Divided by some shade.

Of Hardy's fictional characters it is Marcia Bencomb who is most melodramatically defaced by age. When Pierston first sees her again after an interval of forty years he is impressed by her appearance: ' "You are fair and five-and-thirty – not a day more."' But when she removes her make-up the case is very different:

> She stood the image and superscription of Age – an old woman, pale and shrivelled, her forehead ploughed, her cheek hollow, her hair

white as snow. To this the face he once kissed had been brought by the raspings, chisellings, scourgings, bakings, freezings of forty invidious years – by the thinkings of more than half a lifetime. (*W-B*, 200)

In the serialized version of the novel the contrast between 'the ancient Marcia's aspect' and his recollection of her 'fine former self' afflicts the ailing Pierston with 'a sudden sense of the grotesqueness of things'. The story ends as he is stricken by an agony of hysterical laughter, 'almost too weak to draw breath' (256).

Physical labour can accelerate the process of decline. Ethelberta's carpenter brother, Sol, draws to her attention the shape of his hand:

'Look how my thumb stands out at the root, as if it were out of joint, and that hard place inside there. Did you ever see anything so ugly as that hand – a misshaped monster, isn't he? That comes from the jack-plane, and my pushing against it day after day and year after year.' (*HE*, 297)

George Melbury, as an elderly man, suffers from a 'stiffness about the arm, hip, and knee-joint' and knows 'the origin of every one of these cramps: that in his left shoulder had come of carrying a pollard, unassisted, from Tutcombe Bottom home; that in one leg was caused by the crash of an elm against it when they were felling; that in the other was from lifting a bole' (*Wood*, 25).

More profoundly, if more insidiously, destructive than any physical exertion, however, are 'thinkings' of the kind that have helped to age Marcia Bencomb. The 'perishable tissue' of Clym Yeobright's handsome and relatively youthful face already bears the marks of experience and 'a wearing habit of meditation' – already shows 'that thought is a disease of flesh' (*RN*, 138). Michael Henchard is 'thought-marked' by the time he becomes Mayor (*MC*, 34). When she first appears in *The Woodlanders* Marty South is barely twenty, 'but the necessity of taking thought at a too early period of life had forced the provisional curves of her childhood's face to a premature finality' (9). Pain and care will also leave their mark. The ageing Jocelyn Pierston contemplates his own reflection, like many another Hardy character, and finds that he still appears young for his years:

But there was history in his face – distinct chapters of it; his brow was not that blank page it once had been. He knew the origin of that line in his forehead; it had been traced in the course of a month or two by past troubles. He remembered the coming of this pale wiry hair; it had been brought by the illness in Rome, when he had wished each night that he might never wake again. (*W-B*, 160)

Sue Bridehead has suffered in a comparable way by the time she remarries Phillotson: 'Chastened, world-weary, remorseful, the strain on her nerves had preyed upon her flesh and bones, and she appeared smaller in outline than she had formerly done...' (*Jude*, 389).

In a Hardy novel there is invariably this story behind the story. Whatever the particular plot which is being worked out the human beings concerned are seen to inflict wear or damage and to become worn or damaged in their turn. Melbury is physically strained and exhausted by his exertions in felling trees; his influence on Grace maims Winterborne's life. Pierston, who has been driven by his romantic idealism to hack rocks into statues is eventually reduced by it to white-haired artistic impotence.

It isn't surprising that death is often presented as the natural culmination of such wear and tear: after a lifetime of troubled 'throbbings' the machine gives out. When Arabella listens at the chest of the motionless Jude she finds that

All was still within. The bumping of near thirty years had ceased. (428)

Lady Constantine, in *Two on a Tower*, fears that her despairing love for Swithin may be the death of her:

And as she heard her feverish heart throb against the desk, she firmly believed the wearing impulses of that heart would put an end to her sad life, and momentarily recalled the banished image of St Cleeve to apostrophise him in thoughts that paraphrased the quaint lines of Heine's *Lieb' Liebchen*: –

'Dear my love, press thy hand to my breast, and tell
If thou tracest the knocks in that narrow cell?
A carpenter dwells there; cunning is he,
And slyly he's shaping a coffin for me.' (78)

Her lugubrious premonition is duly fulfilled. In her eventually exhausted state Lady Constantine falls prey to emotional shock:

> Sudden joy after despair had touched an over-strained heart too smartly. Viviette was dead. (281)

Squire Derriman meets a similar fate after being harassed by his nephew, Festus. His body is discovered leaning over a rail:

> On after examination it was found that Uncle Benjy's poor withered heart had cracked and stopped its beating, from damages inflicted on it by the excitements of his life, and of the previous night in particular. (*T-M*, 346)

It's perhaps worthy of remark, in passing, that such foundered machines can have a significant posthumous part to play in Hardy's fiction. Fancy Day reappears when her coffin is opened; Mrs Manston is exhumed; the drowned body of the millwright Halborough is found, after six months, in an unrecognizable state ('A Tragedy of Two Ambitions'). Bellston, in 'The Waiting Supper' is also drowned: 'Every particle of his flesh and clothing had been eaten by fishes or abraded to nothing by the water...' (*Complete Stories*, 586). At least these are decorous remains: 'not a finger or toe-bone missing, so neatly had the aquatic operators done their work'.

The most active and helpful of the cadavers is that of Netty Sargent's uncle. Needing him to sign, or appear to sign, a legal document, in order that she will inherit his house, she keeps him propped up in his chair:

> On the table she laid the large family Bible open before him, and placed his forefinger on the page; and then she opened his eyelids a bit, and put on him his spectacles, so that from behind he appeared for all the world as if he were reading the Scriptures. ('Netty Sargent's Copyhold', *Complete Stories*, 522)

When the agent arrives she steers the dead man's hand to produce an adequate signature.

These episodes reflect Hardy's perennial interest in the morbid and the grotesque, which in turn has much to do with his awareness of the indignities and absurdities to which the 'ephemeral human carcase' may be subjected. His *Life* is studded with folk-anecdotes involving coffins and corpses. 'A good horror has its place in art' he observed when defending 'Barbara of the House of Grebe'.[2] But his occasional flippancy about some particular corpse doesn't mean that he takes death lightly. The element of black humour is by no means incompatible with his more serious intentions.

In 1984 the painter Robert Lenkiewicz reportedly commandeered the body of his deceased friend, Edwin McKenzie, a tramp, had it embalmed and encased it in transparent resin, so that he could keep it by him, 'rather like a large paper-weight'. He was reported as remarking that there was something 'haunting' about his preserved friend: 'One is often rather compelled by the sensations of the total presence of the body, running parallel with the equally total absence of the person'.[3] Hardy would have understood that remark very well. Repeatedly he draws attention to that measureless gulf between the vital character and the declining or defunct body. Perhaps the contrast is most emphatic in *The Dynasts*. At Trafalgar the crew of the "Achille" fight gallantly to the last, knowing that their blazing vessel will be blown to pieces when the fire reaches their powder store:

> The spot is covered now with floating men,
> Some whole, the main in parts; arms, legs, trunks, heads,
> Bobbing with tons of timber on the waves,
> And splinters looped with entrails of the crew. (96)

Mortally wounded, 'stove in', Nelson wishes that the ship's carpenter 'could rig me up a jury-backbone' to take him through the rest of the battle. Although the Admiral is eulogized his corpse is treated with scant respect, being brought home for public burial preserved 'in a cask of sperrits'. A Boatman has heard from Bob Loveday some still more undignified details:

> They were a long time coming, owing to contrary winds, and the "Victory" being little more than a wreck. And grog ran short, because they'd used near all they had to peckle his body in. So – they broached the Adm'l!
> ...the plain calendar of it is, that when he came to be unhooped, it was found that the crew had drunk him dry. (107)

Animal corpses also abound in Hardy's work: Oak's sheep, Durbeyfield's horse, Jude's pig. Jude kills a trapped rabbit to put it out of its misery; Tess kills a number of wounded pheasants. For Hardy a dead bird offers a particularly affecting image. Squire Derriman's fate seems the more pitiable when we read that his 'unconscious carcase was little more than a light empty husk, dry and fleshless as that of a dead heron found on a moor in January' (*T-M*, 346). Shortly after her wedding Elizabeth-Jane finds the present that Henchard had brought her: 'a new bird-cage shrouded in newspaper, and at the bottom of the cage a little ball of feathers – the dead body of a goldfinch' (*MC*, 329). Here, as often in Hardy, there is implied contrast between the beauty and passion of a bird's song and its physical frailty. In 'Shelley's Skylark' he imagines the particular bird that inspired the great ode one day dying, 'A little ball of feather and bone', and later reduced to 'A pinch of unseen, unguarded dust'. In 'Proud Songsters' he makes a similar, but retroactive, observation. The seemingly timeless songs one hears in April are made by

> ... brand-new birds of twelve-months' growing,
> Which a year ago, or less than twain,
> No finches were, nor nightingales,
> Nor thrushes,
> But only particles of grain,
> And earth, and air, and rain.

The observation recalls a comment, already quoted, made by Manston in his final, confessional letter:

> For people are almost always in their graves. When we survey the long race of men, it is strange and still more strange to find that they are mainly dead men, who have scarcely ever been otherwise. (*DR*, 407)

To Hardy the lives of humans and animals alike are brief indeed. The physical organism begins to be worn away as it begins to exist. Just as he displays the omnipresence of sound by recording distinctions or gradations of noise which no normal ear could detect, so he dramatizes by exaggeration the human ageing processes which can so long remain imperceptible.

V

The Well-Beloved would seem to offer Hardy a most unpromising physical environment – one which precludes many of his characteristic effects. Naturally enough 'a solid and single block of limestone four miles long' (9) supports very little in the way of animal life. Indeed it features no more than a single plantation of trees. It is a background, however, that lends itself to metaphor, if not to allegory. The novel offers a simplified, concentrated version of Hardy's view of the inter-involvement of man and the natural environment.

The rock of which the island consists is used by the inhabitants in a variety of ways. The locals construct their houses from it. Various families, including the Pierstons, the Bencombs and the Caros, have built up a successful business by quarrying it. Much of the stone has been exported to London for building purposes. The product encroaches on the world of religion by providing the fabric of St Paul's cathedral (187). It encroaches on art by offering to the likes of Pierston blocks from which a sculpture may be extracted. The rock can be wrought into a place of worship or a statue of Aphrodite.

It could be understood, therefore, as a metaphor for the raw life-energy which can fuel a variety of human enterprises – for example as the sexual instinct which may be disciplined into love for God or aestheticized into works of art. The rock, however, is shown to be a finite resource which is gradually being used up. 'The peninsula carved by Time out of a single stone' (Preface) is being steadily whittled away. The sea continually gnaws at its perimeters. Inland the saws of the quarrymen cut away layer after layer. Pierston visits the wharves in London at which the product is delivered:

> He could occasionally discern the white blocks lying there, vast cubes so persistently nibbled by his parent from his island rock in the English Channel that it seemed as if in time it would be nibbled all away. (51)

At the heart of *The Well-Beloved*, then, is an image of transformation which is also an image of depletion. Hardy is illustrating the process of self-consumption which Lewis Carroll whimsically images in *Through the Looking-Glass* in the sheep which knits. In the act of living we use up ourselves and our environment. This is a central Hardy theme. Pierston touches on it when he says to himself: ' "You cannot live your life and keep it, Jocelyn" ' (160). He makes the observation in the context of reviewing the marks left by time on his own face, a scene which recalls the poem 'I Look into My Glass'. We work too hard, we think too much, we feel too strongly. We use up our inner resources. We act and are acted upon. Hardy makes the point again, and more emphatically, when the ageing Marcia removes her make-up. The harsh forces which have damaged her include the sculptural 'raspings' and 'chisellings'. The obvious inference to be drawn is that as Time carves a peninsula or chisels a human face, eroding and destroying, so the activities of Man, his work, his ambitions, his desires, burn him out. When Pierston first encounters Marcia the 'twanging and spinning storm' without mimics his growing emotional storm within, one of the succession that will eventually exhaust him and leave him white-haired and listless. Man's doings, Man's turbulencies, resemble those of nature.

There is a larger inference, however, perhaps most clearly expressed in the striking passage, quoted in an earlier chapter, which describes the second Avice giving birth (133). It is a studiously symmetrically scene. On the one hand the rock – even cottages of rock; on the other the sea. On the one hand the periodic moans of the woman in labour; on the other the periodic 'throes' of the tide – an 'articulate heave' in either case. On land the light in the cottage; at sea the corresponding beam from the lightship. 'Tamelessness and domesticity' are seen as balanced opposites in that both these lights represent Man's effort to control, to domesticate, vast forces. A doctor is in attendance at the birth, and the lightship gives warning of the treacherous quicksand. But if the flicker of 'domesticity' is common to both halves of the picture so, far more dominantly, is the 'tamelessness'. Avice is not outside it, but caught up in it: 'the travail of the woman within' is all of a piece with 'the travail of the sea without'. They are, at any rate 'in one sense', 'but differing utterances of the selfsame troubled terrestrial Being'. If the Spirit of the Years were on hand he could presumably demonstrate that one and the same impulse is animating the woman in labour and the heaving tide.

Although there is an entire ruined village on the island, 'destroyed by the November gale of 1824', the 'ruins' referred to here are the 'enormous blocks' which have fallen from the Red King's castle. One of them bears the names 'Avice' and 'Jocelyn', though since the inscription goes back twenty years the letters are by now 'nearly worn away by the weather and the brine' (91–2). That Avice, of course, is now dead. In much fresher lettering are the names 'Ann Avice' and 'Isaac' – the second Avice, now pregnant, and her husband. The heaving tides will eventually obliterate these names also. People and the traces they leave are doomed to be washed away. But the 'heaving tides' operate within as well as without. We die from the processes of living. The point made by the passage, and by *The Well-Beloved* as a whole, is that humanbeings are not merely victims of the process of attrition, but also participants in it.

VI

> In the court in front were two worn-out mill-stones, made useful again by being let in level with the ground. Here people stood to smoke and consider things in muddy weather; and cats slept on the clean surfaces when it was hot. (*T-M*, 17)

This may seem a modest afterlife for a millstone, but an afterlife it is, as opposed to mere dissolution. A passage quoted earlier in this chapter noted that the stones of Marygreen church have had a mixed fate: 'either cracked up into heaps of road-metal in the lane, or utilized as pig-sty walls, garden-seats, guard-stones to fences, and rockeries in the flower-beds of the neighbourhood' (*Jude*, 6). Enckworth Court has likewise been converted to a variety of practical local uses, 'old jambs being carried off for rick-staddles, and the foliated timbers of the hall roof making themselves useful as fancy chairs in the summer-houses of rising inns' (*HE*, 229). As Henchard goes downhill, financially and socially, he moves into a cottage 'built of old stones from the long-dismantled Priory, scraps of tracery, moulded window-jambs, and arch-labels, being mixed in with the rubble of the walls' (*MC*, 221). 'A Tryst at an Ancient Earthwork' is located on the site of a Roman fort, but the fort itself has disappeared, dispersed by a similar species of recycling:

> It is a long-violated retreat; all its corner-stones, plinths, and archi-traves were carried away to build neighbouring villages even before medieval or modern history began. Many a block which once may have helped to form a bastion here rests now in broken and dimin-ished shape as part of the chimney-corner of some shepherd's cot-tage within the distant horizon, and the corner-stones of the heathen altar may form the base-course of some adjoining village church. (*Complete Stories*, 649)

The more obvious point here – the ironic one – is the less interesting. The materials of a fortress have been put to peaceful uses; parts of a 'heathen altar' have been absorbed into a Christian church. More intriguing is the mere fact of survival and adaptation. There is evolu-tion of a kind at work here. Raw stone has been shaped to fulfil specific architectural functions, and even when those functions have lapsed it doesn't revert to nullity but retains a modest usefulness.

It is easily perceived that Hardy deals copiously and diversely in deformation, erosion and dissolution. Less obviously, less intensely, but again ubiquitously, he demonstrates possibilites of reformation, recovery and survival. The sort of recycling illustrated above, through which an abandoned building is absorbed into several new ones – usually of humbler status – is a relatively straightforward example of this kind.

Hardy can't be rightly appreciated if this aspect of his work is underrated. In this context it might be instructive to compare him with a hyperbolic writer of quite another cast – Jonathan Swift. In *Gulliver's Travels* the hero voyages to the land of the giant Brobdingnagians. Although they are in general a friendly, peacable race, unlike the mean-spirited Lilliputians previously visited, Gulliver finds himself physically repelled by them. In a famous passage he describes his revulsion at the sight of a huge, freckled female breast and his disgust at the bodily smells of his kindly hosts. The book has been praised for the keenness of its satire against human physical limitations; but surely the compliment is based on a misconception. If Swift intended his satire to be so read he was guilty of an unlikely obtuseness. The voyages to Lilliput and Brobdingnag are based on a 12:1 scale: the Lilliputians are one twelfth the size of an average human being, while the Brobdingnagians are twelve times as large. What would be the point of asserting that were we to smell twelve times as pungent as we do the effect would be unpleasant? Of course it would be. But happily – and by definition – that is not the case: we are what we are.

The point being made is surely a more interesting one. Here, as in the fourth book of *Gulliver's Travels* and the 'Digression on Madness' in *A Tale of a Tub*, Swift lets the satire double back on himself. What is indicted is his own weakness – the morbid hypersensitivity which results in a morally and sexually incapacitating exaggeration of human limitations.

Hardy, of course, is open to comparable accusations of morbid over-sensitivity, of hyperbolic insistence on the brevity of life and love. It was hinted above that he might conceivably be identified with Little Time, a character too consumed with his awareness of transience to enjoy *anything*. But the charge doesn't stick. Hardy needn't, like Swift, apologize for inhuman extremities of pessimism.

The obvious initial point to make in this context concerns his remarkable capacity for conveying a sense of cheerfulness, good fellowship, love or joy. Loss and disappointment show keenly in his work precisely because converse feelings have been warmly and vividly dramatized. But this chapter has been implying a defence of a different kind. Hardy was concerned not only with transience but also with various forms of continuity and transformation. Seasons change, trees and buildings fall, people and animals die – but the process continues and renews itself. A diary note from a period of sickness puts the case casually and impartially:

> Incidents of lying in bed for months. Skin gets fair: corns take their leave: feet and toes grow shapely as those of a Greek statue. Keys get rusty; watch dim, boots mildewed; hat and clothes old-fashioned; umbrella eaten out with rust; children seen through the window are grown taller. (*Life*, 152)

Over a brief representative period of time some things have faded or decayed, others have been renewed. Hardy's fiction similarly shows that among the powers at work in the world are forces of healing, growth and regeneration: the Henchards come together again; Farfrae builds up a business; Jude educates himself; Oak marries Bathsheba; Tess rediscovers joy.

Even death, for Hardy, has only a limited conclusiveness. The repeated references to recycled stonework illustrate some of the varying possibilities of survival and adaptation. There is a grisly example of a comparable kind in *The Hand of Ethelberta*, where dead trees, with the branches sawn back, serve as 'huge hat-stand(s)' from which joints of horse-meat are suspended (139). More hearteningly in *The Well-Beloved* slow geological reworking has petrified trees into part of the stony substance of the Isle of Singers: at least to some extent the eroded island can renew itself. At the human level there are comparable 'Transformations':

> Portion of this yew
> Is a man my grandsire knew,
> Bosomed here at its foot:
> This branch may be his wife,
> A ruddy human life
> Now turned to a green shoot ...
>
> So, they are not under ground,
> But as nerves and veins abound

> In the growths of upper air,
> And they feel the sun and rain,
> And the energy again
> That made them what they were!

The poem recalls several on this and closely related themes. They
include 'Friends Beyond', 'Voices from Things Growing in a
Churchyard' and 'Drummer Hodge'. Hodge will become part of the
veldt where he dies, his 'homely Northern breast and brain' growing
into 'some Southern tree'. Hardy speculates in a similar vein about the
fate of 'Shelley's Skylark':

> Maybe it rests in the loam I view,
> Maybe it throbs in a myrtle's green,
> Maybe it sleeps in the coming hue
> Of a grape on the slopes of yon inland scene.

Since in 'Proud Songsters' he sees nightingales, thrushes and other
birds as being conjured from 'particles of grain,/And earth, and air, and
rain', the skylark which has 'perished' might after all perhaps be seen
as undergoing a radical species of hibernation. This isn't, however, the
point which Hardy seems to be making in 'Shelley's Skylark', even
though it is there to be made. He asserts that the bird has already
achieved 'immortality':

> For it inspired a bard to win
> Ecstatic heights in thought and rhyme.

The skylark survives in art, and as an idea.

Hardy rarely refers elsewhere to the 'immortalizing' potentiality of
art, but the transformation into 'idea' is a favourite theme, and takes a
variety of forms. His description, in *The Trumpet-Major*, of the departure
of the *Victory*, offers one version of the process. The vessel is first seen
in substantial terms as 'The great silent ship, with her population of
blue-jackets, marines, officers, captain, and…admiral', but she passes
'like a phantom'. As she recedes her appearance changes:

> Sometimes her aspect was that of a large white bat, sometimes that
> of a grey one. In the course of time the watching girl saw that the
> ship had passed her nearest point; the breadth of her sails diminished
> by foreshortening, till she assumed the form of an egg on end. (292)

Later her width contracts 'to the proportion of a feather', and eventually she seems 'no more than a dead fly's wing on a sheet of spider's web'. The diminution, the increasing insubstantiality, sketch the transition from workaday vessel through physical impairment to historic legend.

For Hardy it is usually and chiefly love that brings about this kind of 'transformation'. Troy's love for Fanny flares into renewed life when he sees her coffin. When Pierston hears that Avice Caro has died his mental image of her is transformed: 'He loved the woman dead and inaccessible as he had never loved her in life' (*W-B*, 72). Smith and Knight find their old love similarly revived when they learn of the death of Elfride. Rather unnervingly Hardy himself, years after the publication of any of these novels, was to respond in an identical spirit to the sudden death of his first wife. In the 1912/13 sequence the person recently living, and not greatly loved, is translated into 'A phantom of his own figuring', 'A ghost-girl-rider', an object of tender devotion.

'Logs on the Hearth' is subtitled 'A Memory of a Sister'. Thanks to memory the apple-tree now chopped up into fire-logs can give up a beautiful ghost. Hardy recalls the sister who used to climb the tree with him, and the poem ends joyfully with the past episode forcing itself into the present tense:

> My fellow-climber rises dim
>   From her chilly grave –
> Just as she was, her foot near mine on the bending limb,
> Laughing, her young brown hand awave.

The abstract perpetuation which Hardy's memory affords Emma and his sister is presented as only a limited possibility and a short-term solace. 'Her Immortality' makes that point clear: such an afterlife for a loved one must die with the person who recalls him or her. The inescapable truth is that the intenser joys of which our combination of flesh and mind makes us uniquely capable cannot last. But there are consolations, if of a muted sort. The physical survives through one set of translations, the conceptual through another. Beyond both these possibilities is a vision of the workings of nature which subsumes all such transformations into circling patterns of energy and movement, at once superhuman and subhuman.

6
Concatenations

Painting lends itself to explication by lecture. On a screen, conveniently magnified, is the work to be discussed – perhaps a landscape with figures – with all its particularities on simultaneous display. The lecturer's pointer can swiftly draw attention to the shepherd in the foreground, to the windmill in the background, to this crag, that tree, those clouds. There, plain to the eyes of the audience, are the details to be held in suspension, instantly available for conceptual cross-relation. The pattern to be discussed is accessible to the eye while the speaker has freedom to invade the ear. Even if the lecture should later be incorporated into a book the case need not be greatly altered. The picture may be reproduced, and the reader can shuttle freely between illustration and extended verbal discussion.

Nor would the commentator feel called upon to justify such an analytical exercise. By definition painting involves cross-relationship. The mere fact that shepherd and windmill, for example, are included in the same three-dimensional framework means that they have, or should have, something to do with one another, certainly in compositional and probably in conceptual terms. A serious work in the landscape tradition isn't expected to contain 'irrelevant' material.

The case is rather different for the literary critic who wishes, as I do, to suggest that a novel can or should be read very much as a landscape painting is 'read'. The descriptive details concerned – the equivalents of the windmill, the crag and the clouds – may seem to be haphazardly scattered along the length of the narrative. It is far from self-evident that the reader should, or even could, apprehend them simultaneously. The novel, it could be argued, offers not one picture but a whole series of pictures. Why should the snowstorm in chapter three have anything to do with the rain-shower in chapter eight, perhaps an hour's reading-time further on? Might it not, in fact, have been superfluous, strictly speaking, even to its immediate context? Fiction is a notoriously impure medium, hospitable to all sorts of enabling or even superfluous matter. Texts can shift or shrink. A Hardy or a Dickens might effect substantial changes between serial and hard-cover publication. A particularly lengthy work, such as *Clarissa*, may be made available, even for university study, in a heavily abridged version. Since so much fictional material is seemingly dispensable the significance of this or that detail can't be taken for granted. Few would dispute that Hardy is a powerful descriptive writer, but the claim that descriptive detail is intrinsic to the very meaning of his fiction is one that must be made good.

To press that case one would ideally like to emulate the art-lecturer and begin by displaying the elements concerned – here a tree, there a worn threshold, here a hailstorm, there an old inn. But as this book may already have made too clear, there could not be an exhaustive account of this kind: the material is too abundant. In any case mere listing wouldn't be enough. As implied earlier, one would want these descriptive set-pieces and fragments to be somehow exhibited stereoscopically, to show how they are distributed variously along the tunnel-like length of the narrative concerned.

In the absence of such possibilities the obvious resort must be, after all, to the broad categorizations and the selections of examples that have characterized this book. There is, however, an alternative mode of illustration. At various points in any Hardy novel there are to be found passages of extreme descriptive intensity where many of the elements separately discussed in this book are crowded together in vivid concentration. These episodes of convergence or concatenation can be so densely detailed as to move well beyond the requirements of realism. The calculated over-elaboration invites a response at the level of expressionism or surrealism. Such passages are often memorable in their own right; they can also give the reader a renewed and sharper sense of the descriptive energies animating the narrative at large. The local exercise in patterning and metaphor recapitulates the workings of the novel as a whole.

In the pages that follow I will be looking closely at four such passages, with a view to showing how they display, in shorthand form, the patterns of Hardy's imaginative vision. It is neither accidental nor inappropriate that the readings proposed involve the kind of detailed analysis usually reserved for poetry. The novels everywhere display a poet's vision and a poet's technique.

I

Somerset looked down on the mouth of the tunnel. The absurdity of the popular commonplace that science, steam, and travel must always be unromantic and hideous, was proved on the spot. On either slope of the deep cutting, green with long grass, grew drooping young trees of ash, beech, and other flexible varieties, their foliage almost concealing the actual railway which ran along the bottom, its thin steel rails gleaming like silver threads in the depths. The vertical front of the tunnel, faced with brick that had once been red, was now weather-stained, lichened, and mossed over in harmonious hues of rusty-browns, pearly greys, and neutral greens, at the very base appearing a little blue-black spot like a mouse-hole – the tunnel's mouth...

Down Somerset plunged through the long grass, bushes, late summer flowers, moths, and caterpillars, vexed with himself that he had come there, since Paula was so inscrutable, and humming the notes of some song he did not know. The tunnel that had seemed so small from the surface was a vast archway when he reached its mouth, which emitted, as a contrast to the sultry heat on the slopes of the cutting, a cool breeze, that had travelled a mile underground from the other end. Far away in the darkness of this silent subterranean corridor he could see the other end as a mere speck of light.

When he had conscientiously admired the construction of the massive archivault, and the majesty of its nude ungarnished walls, he looked up the slope at the carriage; it was so small to the eye that it might have been made for a performance by canaries; Paula's face being still smaller, as she leaned back in her seat, idly looking down at him. There seemed something roguish in her attitude of criticism, and to be no longer the subject of her contemplation he entered the tunnel out of her sight.

In the middle of the speck of light before him appeared a speck of black; and then a shrill whistle, dulled by millions of tons of earth, reached his ears from thence. It was what he had been on his guard against all the time, – a passing train; and instead of taking the trouble to come out of the tunnel he stepped into a recess, till the train had rattled past, and vanished onward round a curve.

Somerset still remained where he had placed himself, mentally balancing science against art, the grandeur of this fine piece of construction against that of the castle, and thinking whether Paula's

father had not, after all, the best of it, when all at once he saw
Paula's form confronting him at the entrance of the tunnel. He
instantly went forward into the light where she was; to his surprise
she was as pale as a lily. (*Lao*, Ch. XII)

If *A Laodicean* isn't Hardy's worst novel it is certainly a contender for
the title. But its failings are no doubt largely attributable to the serious
illness which afflicted the author after the completion of 'the early
chapters', and obliged him to dictate most of the rest of it from his
sick-bed. The controlling ideas were promising and there are some
vivid pulses of life in the novel. The episode of the railway-cutting has
an oddity and energy that would have graced a better book.

In several ways it recalls 'A Tryst at an Ancient Earthwork', a story
which will be discussed later in this chapter. Indeed the tunnel *is* an
'earthwork' of sorts. Its mouth emits 'a cool breeze', just as the fortification in 'A Tryst' seems to 'breathe out' a gale. Like the earthwork it is
barely distinguishable from a natural formation: the massive human
intervention in the landscape is hidden. ' "If it were not a railway we
should call it a lovely dell," ' remarks Mrs Goodman. There are large
powers, human and natural, at work in entanglement. The cutting has,
like the earthwork, its own ecology – in this case flexible trees, 'long
grass, bushes, late summer flowers, moths, and caterpillars'. To explore
either the tunnel or the fortress involves climbing and descending and
subjection to curious shifts of proportion and perception: 'The tunnel
that had seemed so small from the surface was a vast archway when he
reached its mouth'.

The episode differs from 'A Tryst' in that instead of being an isolated
fragment it is an important step in a developing plot-sequence. Its
immediate narrative function is simple enough. Like the sword-play
scene in *Far from the Madding Crowd*, or the cliff scene in *A Pair of Blue
Eyes* or the scene of the flooded road in *Tess*, it accelerates a dawning
relationship by throwing the couple concerned into physical contact.
The shriek of an oncoming train, as Somerset and Paula are crossing
the track, has them rushing away, hand in hand. In functional terms
this sort of device is familiar from popular romantic fiction, where it
tends towards some such conclusion as: 'they found themselves in one
another's arms'. But whereas in that context the whole point would be
the achievement of the romantic clinch, in Hardy the interest is heavily
concentrated on the attendant circumstance. The required plot devel-
opment seems to have provided a convenient occasion for the episode
and the description, rather than vice-versa.

Jane Austen's work, and in particular *Sense and Sensibility*, offers a defining negative analogy. The 'figures' in these indoor novels are occasionally released into the landscape, but only on the strict condition that they remain unaffected by it. Marianne Dashwood climbs the downs, 'attracted by the partial sunshine of a showery sky', and is soon enjoying 'the animating gales of an high south-westerly wind'. When it begins to rain she runs down the hill at top speed – and is promptly punished for her recklessness by spraining her ankle.[1] There is a longer-term penalty in that the accident introduces her to Willoughby, who is to break her heart. Later, when Marianne is staying at Cleveland, a 'delightful twilight walk' in the wilder part of the grounds, 'where the trees were the oldest, and the grass was the longest and wettest' so exacerbates an existing cold as to bring her to the brink of death.[2] These are follies which she later repents. Austen's stance is clear. It is dangerous to allow one's mood to be modified by the beauties or energies of nature: social conduct is the thing.

Although Paula chides Somerset for his thoughtlessness in giving her a scare, social conduct clearly *isn't* the thing for Hardy – or, rather, it's one thing among many. Surely any serious reader will feel that the description of the cutting somehow matters in its own right. But how? What is it *for*? What does it *do*?

Through comparison with other novels one can see that it forms part of a familiar Hardy sequence. His stories are always love stories, and the love is almost invariably dramatized through a series of episodes involving physical turbulence or disequilibrium and extravagant natural description. The most conventional form of such turbulence is the dancing in which music and motion will excite susceptible partners and perhaps even exalt them into an ecstatic trance. Sometimes, however, the couple are literally 'transported' – bodily whisked away – by a horse, a gig, a train, a boat. More melodramatically the weather amid which Hardy's lovers move tends towards extremes. Oak and Bathsheba, Swithin and Viviette, Pierston and Marcia, Cytherea and Manston are among the couples caught together in fierce storms, the tempestuous conditions both prompting and mimicking the excesses of romantic passion.

At the wedding which concludes *Under the Greenwood Tree* Mrs Penny remarks: ' "Well 'tis humps and hollers with the best of us" ' (195–6). Hardy goes a long way towards interpreting this dictum in literal terms. His lovers can be projected high into the air – on a hay-rick, up a tree, on the tower of Endelstow church or Rouen Cathedral. Viviette and Swithin clutch one another, aloft in the observatory, as a sudden hurricane whips away the dome that has been standing between them and the stars. Similarly, strange depths or descents can open before Hardy's lovers – a church vault, a cliff face, a hollow amid the ferns. Perceptions are giddily shifted as these physical perturbations mirror emotional ones. The effect is brilliantly caught in a special case, the poem 'After a Journey'. Hardy has returned to Cornwall, going back forty years to re-encounter the spirit of the young Emma. Disorientation in time and feeling is expressed through disorientation is space:

> Hereto I come to view a voiceless ghost;
>   Whither, O whither will its whim now draw me?
> Up the cliff, down, till I'm lonely, lost,
>   And the unseen waters' ejaculations awe me.
> Where you will next be there's no knowing,
>   Facing round about me everywhere,
>   With your nut-coloured hair,
> And gray eyes, and rose-flush coming and going.

The speaker cannot be physically placed, the movement of the verse is vertiginous, the sense and even the grammar uncertain. This is the kind of confusion which Hardy habitually associates with falling in love, and habitually dramatizes through physical images of movement, sound, danger and disequilibrium.

Somerset, as it happens, is subjected to pretty well the full range of such experiences. His early encounters with Paula, as he begins to fall in love with her, have much to do with the great tower of Stancy Castle. For a time he is trapped there, in a turret room. Later he sees Paula 'standing at the top of the tower looking over the parapet upon him' (86) and holding the handkerchief he had left in the turret-window as a signal for help.

Shortly after their encounter in the railway cutting Paula gives a party at which he is able to dance with her for the first time. Lost in bliss he feels as though 'human beings were shaking themselves free of all inconvenient gravitation':

> Somerset's feelings burst from his lips. 'This is the happiest moment I have ever known,' he said. 'Do you know why?'
> 'I think I saw a flash of lightning through the opening of the tent,' said Paula, with roguish abruptness. (120)

She is right, of course, as the seasoned reader of Hardy could have predicted: 'Within a few minutes a long growl of thunder was heard'. When the dance ends they go for a stroll and are trapped in the summer-house in a full-blooded storm. Somerset takes the providential opportunity of declaring his love – albeit to uncertain effect. The first sequence in the romantic roller-coaster ride is completed, with its ups and downs and turmoils.

The episode of the railway cutting offers a starting point for an inquiry into the workings of such episodes and sequences in general. Their metaphorical and associative implications are far from simple. It is often said, for example, that the sword-play scene in *Far from the Madding Crowd* is a metaphor for seduction. The claim is too narrow. At a basic level the episode functions as a shorthand form. A relationship which would have taken several chapters to establish in terms of social encounters is defined and brought to a critical point in a few pages. Moreover that definition goes well beyond the social. Hardy needs to provide an explanation, even an apologia, for Bathsheba's infatuation with a shallow philanderer, given that she has resisted the advances of two far worthier suitors. Accordingly he devises an episode which offers a sort of X-ray picture of her feelings. We see what aspects of Troy attract her – command, athleticism, exoticism, dangerousness, sexual sophistication and aggression. There is also a response to the sensuality of the summer evening – the late sunlight, the caressing foliage. Although the chapter closes with the kiss which advances the narrative the episode has been too hyperbolic to invite merely a literal reading. It is located somewhere between the depiction of socialized emotions normally found in realist fiction and the visionary disclosure of essential responses offered in *The Dynasts*.

The shifts in perspective in the *Laodicean* passage are similarly expressive. Hurt by Paula's 'inscrutability' Somerset turns away from her and puts a distance between them. The tunnel and his professional appraisal of it loom larger in his mind, and Paula dwindles. Later they are drawn together again when she shows agitation on his behalf, and within moments they are hand in hand, after a narrow escape from death. As in the sword-play episode, what is presented as a chapter in their outer life is effectively a transcription of a chapter, even of several chapters, in their inner life. In the normal course of events the lovers' feelings about one another would oscillate perhaps less violently, but with something of this variety and extremity.

These emotions are also somehow enlarged and aggrandized by association with the lush vegetation, the massive railway cutting, the speeding, rattling train. What could have seemed mere tiffs and mood-shifts are given drama and energy. Like the sword-play scene, or the chess-games in *A Pair of Blue Eyes*, the episode is an exposition of suppressed emotions, something not unlike an operatic duet. Operatic music can project the passions which the libretto merely alludes to. Even in a quasi-domestic context, as, for example, in *La Traviata* or *La Bohème*, the convention is that the protagonist's musical utterances are proportioned to the intensity of his or her love. In the fiction of the Victorian period a roughly comparable effect is often achieved through lavish metaphor. Lucy Snowe seizes on the letter sent to her by Dr John: '... it was the wild savoury mess of the hunter, nourishing and salubrious meat, forest-fed or desert-reared, fresh, healthful, and life-sustaining'.[3] Dorothea's 'ideas and resolves', in the disillusionment of marriage to Casaubon, 'seemed like melting ice floating and lost in the warm flood of which they been but another form'.[4] Hardy doesn't reject the technique, but his best metaphors are tacit or indirect. He invokes natural description both to imply powerful feelings and to magnify the reader's sense of them. Somerset's love for Paula partakes of various of the responses elicited by the cutting itself and the episode to which it gives rise – fascination, respect, admiration, excitement, apprehension, protectiveness, warmth, resentment.

The portrayal of Eustacia Vye is perhaps the aptest illustration of this metaphorical, or associative, method. Hardy describes her as 'not altogether unlovable' (*RN*, 68), and she has had her academic admirers, but a significant number of critics have found the character inadequate to the tragic role she seems to have been assigned. The disagreement would seem to relate to the fact that she is presented in two quite distinct ways. If her moral and social conduct is analysed it's difficult not to conclude that she is a self-dramatizing egotist, amoral, indolent, naive and emotionally unstable. But although Hardy provides the sort of evidence from which such inferences might be drawn he also offers a presentation of a quite different kind, based on association and metaphor. He virtually allows her to live up to her self-dramatization. Eustacia is linked with fire, with darkness, with the moon. She is summoned to nocturnal assignations by the sound of a splash, or the sight of a moth. She is seen walking the heath alone, or poised at the summit of a tor, peering through a telescope. The first time she hears Clym mentioned it is by disembodied voices emerging from the length of a chimney. The first time she encounters him in person he is merely a greeting emerging from the darkness. Meeting her former lover, Wildeve, at a time when her marriage is faltering, she dances with him in the open air, half hypnotized by the motion and by the moonlight. By means of such images Hardy presents the alternative Eustacia, whose capacity for passionate love 'raised her as a soul' (118). They chart and figure her intensities. The inconsistency of Paula Power, the Laodicean, is comparably presented. In the social context she is chary of any direct expression of romantic feeling. What happens in the cutting is among other things an involuntary self-disclosure.

An essential feature of the chapter can easily elude analysis. The description is undeniably, even comically, full of sexual suggestiveness. The difficulty for the reader or critic lies not in recognizing this element but in deciding how to interpret it and respond to it.

In Howard Jacobson's *Peeping Tom*, a comic novel which offers a fancifully satirical account of Hardy's sexual proclivities, there is a relevant scene. A Freudian lecturer sketches on the blackboard what purports to be the subterranean rock-formation described in 'Our Exploits at West Poley'. Although she seems to be following Hardy's account in some detail the finished picture shows what the author is said to have involuntarily described: a 'giant yawning vulva'.[5] If there's a joke here it could well have been Hardy's before it was Jacobson's. The 'West Poley' passage is far from being the only one in Hardy available for this sort of treatment. In fact Jacobson, who shows close knowledge of the fiction, may well have thought hard before picking that particular description in preference to 'The Hollow Amid the Ferns' in *Far from the Madding Crowd*, or the *Laodicean* passage quoted here. Alternatively Hardy's own illustration to 'The Dance at the Phoenix', in *Wessex Poems*, could have been invoked.

The incident from *A Laodicean* might seem to have advantages in offering not merely a relevant physical configuration but an orgasmic moment when, with 'a noise and shriek', a train rushes past the lovers, 'causing Paula's dress, hair, and ribbons to flutter violently, and blowing up the fallen leaves in a shower over their shoulders' (98). By the time the couple have clambered back to the road the mood has undergone the equivalent of a post-coital change: 'the tunnel-cutting appeared a dreary gulf enough now to the young man ...'.

Since I concur, as Jacobson apparently does, with Ally Sloper's dictum that 'a dirty mind is a continual feast', I have no desire to be pompous about *Peeping Tom*, where there is a good, productive joke at work. But it is a joke which badly misrepresents Hardy, who is candidly interested in sexual attraction and unembarrassed by it. Where there is *double entendre* in his work it is unlikely to be involuntary. Nor – although he is capable of sardonic jokes about sex, as about other topics – will it necessarily be funny. Hardy deals in *double entendre* in the basic sense of wanting to suggest two things simultaneously: he doesn't say one thing simply as an oblique way of saying another. 'The Ivy-Wife', earlier discussed, is a case in point. It isn't a poem that pretends to be about ivy, but is really about a certain kind of woman. It is about both. That is the very point of it. The doings of the ivy and the doings of the 'wife' are so similar as to be virtually identical – manifestations of a common instinct.

Something very like this can be the case in Hardy even when the significances concerned are multiple rather than dual. It is an obtuseness of our own time to assume that in any such instance the sexual implication is what 'really' matters, either because it is the comic *raison d'être* of the passage concerned, or because the author is assumed to have lapsed into unconscious self-revelation. That assumption is rarely likely to be applicable to Hardy. He deals in numerous mutually qualifying themes, of which the sexual is but one. The huge cleft that Man has gouged out of the hill has already been overgrown by nature. Indifferent insects inhabit it. Yet the achievement has been so colossal that a breeze can now blow for a mile underground. There is an implied comparison between the tunnel bored through the earth and the telegraph-wire that threads the sky to reach Stancey Castle. The architecture of the late Mr Power is compared with the work of the castle-builder. The 'grandeur' of the manmade tunnel is a context for the countervailing hint that the individual human being is no more than a speck upon a speck. The sexual and romantic impulses of the lovers are brought into close contiguity with sudden death. They could be felt to have the stifled immediacy of 'a shrill whistle, dulled by millions of tons of earth'. Again, an awareness of these ironies and associations can be felt to inform Somerset's feelings towards Paula.

All these explanations tend towards implying that the episode makes some kind of complicated sense as a whole – that its disparate parts cross-relate, that characters and context are inter-involved. But this emphasis must not be allowed to obscure the sudden incongruity of the passage – which is what makes it intriguing in the first place. Rosemary Sumner has drawn attention to the surrealistic element in Hardy's fiction, proposing comparisons with, for example, the work of Magritte.[6] Her suggestion is apt. The Magritte painting 'Time Suspended', shows a diminutive express train bursting from an empty fireplace into a staid middle-class sitting-room. Although it isn't difficult, after reflection, to propose various 'explanations' of the image the strangeness of it is what first captures the attention, and also what makes 'explanation' seem both necessary yet ultimately impossible. The scene of the railway-cutting offers a similar effect in reverse: instead of the energies of the train intruding on the proprieties of bourgeois life it is decorous middle-class romance which has somehow strayed into the domain of locomotive power and been redefined by it.

II

It was a typical summer evening in June, the atmosphere being in such delicate equilibrium and so transmissive that inanimate objects seemed endowed with two or three senses, if not five. There was no distinction between the near and the far, and an auditor felt close to everything within the horizon. The soundlessness impressed her as a positive entity rather than as the mere negation of noise. It was broken by the strumming of strings.

Tess had heard those notes in the attic above her head. Dim, flattened, constrained by their confinement, they had never appealed to her as now, when they wandered in the still air with a stark quality like that of nudity. To speak absolutely, both instrument and execution were poor; but the relative is all, and as she listened Tess, like a fascinated bird, could not leave the spot. Far from leaving she drew up towards the performer, keeping behind the hedge that he might not guess her presence.

The outskirt of the garden in which Tess found herself had been left uncultivated for some years, and was now damp and rank with juicy grass which sent up mists of pollen at a touch, and with tall blooming weeds emitting offensive smells – weeds whose red and yellow and purple hues formed a polychrome as dazzling as that of cultivated flowers. She went stealthily as a cat through this profusion of growth, gathering cuckoo-spittle on her skirts, cracking snails that were underfoot, staining her hands with thistle-milk and slug-slime, and rubbing off upon her naked arms sticky blights which, though snow-white on the apple-tree-trunks, made madder stains on her skin; thus she drew near to Clare, still unobserved of him.

Tess was conscious of neither time nor space. The exaltation which she had described as being producible at will by gazing at a star, came now without any determination of hers; she undulated upon the thin notes of the second-hand harp, and their harmonies passed like breezes through her, bringing tears into her eyes. The floating pollen seemed to be his notes made visible, and the dampness of the garden the weeping of the garden's sensibility. Though near nightfall, the rank-smelling weed-flowers glowed as if they would not close, for intentness, and the waves of colour mixed with the waves of sound. (*Tess*, Ch. XIX)

This is perhaps the most discussed passage in Hardy's fiction: it has been both admired and criticized. The arguments about it go back for years in a series of Chinese boxes: there have been comments upon comments upon comments. They would seem to derive from a widespread sense that this is a passage close to the heart of Hardy's enterprise. Stylistically and thematically it is instantly recognizable as his handiwork, but that is only part of the point. This is a load-bearing episode, perceived to be a turning-point at the centre of perhaps his greatest novel. It seems to offer a partial explanation of Tess's, and Hardy's own, sense of the complexity and cruelty of being alive. If, despite its distinctiveness and force, it seems ultimately specious the implications for Hardy's art are very damaging. It is in any case an obvious topic for discussion in this book since it suggests a particularly subtle and powerful relationship, full of tensions and seeming contradictions, between 'figure' and 'landscape'.

The matter-of-fact beginning is characteristic. Hardy likes to establish a context of time and season. The opening phrase of the novel is 'On an evening in the latter part of May'. When Tess sets out for Chaseborough 'It was a fine September evening, just before sunset' (65). When 'Phase the Second' begins 'It was a Sunday morning in late October' (81). In the two latter cases, incidentally, as in the garden scene, it is dusk or daybreak, Hardy's favoured fictional time, when 'the constraint of day and the suspense of night neutralise each other, leaving absolute mental liberty' (91). In all three descriptions there is a scrupulosity of detail which strongly implies that the time, the light, and the perceived mood of nature are essential to the significance of what is taking place. In the garden scene, however, the explanation is curiously abstract: 'the atmosphere being in such delicate equilibrium and so transmissive that inanimate objects seemed endowed with two or three senses, if not five'. David Lodge, in his interesting account of the episode, claims that this first paragraph shows Hardy at 'his most ponderous'.[7] To me it seems merely that he is striving for an accurate account of an elusive effect. I take it that 'delicate equilibrium' implies that no one entity in the scene particularly attracts the attention: the light is fading and the air is motionless and soundless. But what does it mean to say that the atmosphere is 'transmissive'? Presumably that in this stillness, and absence of highlights, all visible objects seem to partake of one another in balanced mutual awareness. The sound of the harp is to destroy, or rather to usurp, this equilibrium. The scents, the colours, the textures are to be perceived by Tess in relationship to the music rather than to one another.

Tess is alone. As so often in Hardy the love-sensation is experienced in solitude. He regularly creates tableaux in which a loved one, or potential loved one, is seen asleep by the protagonist, a passive subject for meditation. Here Clare is present to Tess only through his playing. Lodge speculates about the repeated emphasis on the relative mediocrity of the music. Surely Hardy's point here is the simple one that for the purposes of the episode the *quality* of the music is not the issue it often can be in his work. Angel is not a Manston or even a Farfrae. The affinity is rather with the Aeolian harp incident in *The Trumpet-Major*. The notes Tess hears have only to be appealing enough to elicit from her imagination some abstract sense of an ideal of beauty or of love.

The surroundings which dramatize Tess's response serve to intensify it. Everything becomes relevant to what she feels. The passage is characterized above all by profusion and fecundity. A great many things and kinds of thing are sensually apprehended as over-brimmingly alive. The seemingly still and passive scene is endlessly active. Almost everything described goes beyond itself in terms of exhalation, exudation or transformation.

The adjective 'transmissive' in the first paragraph is an invitation to a synaesthetic response. One kind of sensory experience shades into another. Everywhere there are echoes, doublings. Tess has 'naked arms': the notes of the harp have a quality 'of nudity'. The notes wander: the pollen floats. Tess has tears in her eyes: the garden seems to weep. She 'undulates': the colour and the sound are generalized into mingling waves. Her experience becomes one thing, a complex totality appealing simultaneously to sight, hearing, smell, touch, imagination and emotion.

It has often been noted as a puzzling aspect of the scene that it bewilderingly mingles the appealing with the disagreeable. On the one hand wandering music, a dazzling polychrome of flowers, mists of pollen. On the other offensive smells, slime, sticky blights. Implied, of course, in this heavily erotic description is the bewilderingly compound experience of love and sex. Lodge is surely right in finding a 'sensuous relish'[8] in the texture even of the language describing some of the apparently disagreeable details – the 'cuckoo-spittle', 'thistle-milk' and 'slug-slime'. Hardy is not proposing a simple opposition between base sexual desire and the loftier spiritual or imaginative elements of love. Tess responds by animal instinct – like a cat or a bird – on the way to reaching her state of 'exaltation'. Even the grossly physical shades into, and helps to engender, the ethereal: from the rank, juicy grass floats the pollen which seems to be Angel's 'notes made visible'. Tess's clothes, and her very skin, have been dampened and stained by the slimes and juices of the garden, but, in her own terms, her soul has escaped, leaving these physical soilings behind. Once again Hardy is dealing in his own detached brand of *double entendre*. If the tall, sticky, smelly plants are sexually suggestive, so, in a complementary sense, are the wandering music, the weeping garden, the rapt intentness. Sensations, ideas, ideals coalesce. For Hardy love, in its very nature, is a kind of *double entendre*.

The scene offers a most striking image of the duality central to the novel, but it is one of a series of such images in *Tess*, which mutually explain, mutually qualify. A comparable, if humbler, sense of transformation has been shown to elevate the drinkers at Rolliver's inn:

> The stage of mental comfort to which they had arrived at this hour was one wherein their souls expanded beyond their skins, and spread their personalities warmly through the room. In this process the chamber and its furniture grew more and more dignified and luxurious, the shawl hanging at the window took upon itself the richness of tapestry, the brass handles of the chest of drawers were as golden knockers, and the carved bedposts seemed to have some kinship with the magnificent pillars of Solomon's temple. (31)

The dancers at Chaseborough, who have also been drinking, modulate similarly between the the physical and the ideal. Here is another evening scene, with music playing and the air clouded with peat-dust, which forms 'a sort of vegeto-human pollen' (66). The whirling dancers can look like demi-gods to Tess's eyes, but outside 'resolved themselves into the homely personalities of her own next-door neighbours' (67). At the high point of the evening 'the ecstasy and the dream began, in which emotion was the matter of the universe, and matter but an adventitious intrusion likely to hinder you from spinning where you wanted to spin' (67). The idyll is interrupted by a sudden 'dull thump', as the tipsy dancers trip over one another and collapse into 'a twitching entanglement of arms and legs'.

Hardy maintains the paradox as he describes the journey home of these revellers. Though they would appear 'terrestrial and lumpy ... to the mean unglamoured eye' their own apprehension is very different.

Their sense is 'that they were soaring along in a supporting medium, possessed of original and profound thoughts; themselves and surrounding nature forming an organism of which all the parts harmoniously and joyously interpenetrated each other' (69). Even when the drunken Car Darch strips off her bodice to fight Tess her body appears 'as luminous and beautiful as some Praxitelean creation' (70).

The Chaseborough scenes were part of a section omitted from the serialized version of *Tess* and published separately as 'Saturday Night in Arcady'. They culminate, of course, in the seduction of the heroine, and provide, with their tensions and dualities, an oblique commentary on that happening and the instincts and emotions involved in it. In a comparable way the garden scene provides a further perspective on the love between Angel and Tess. Angel's own idealizing tendency is to be made abundantly clear: he comes to see Tess not as herself but as 'a visionary essence of woman' (134). When he claims, after her confession to him, that 'the woman I have been loving is not you' (226), for better or worse he is speaking the truth. He has responded to her 'music' – has known her as an idea, not as an individual. Tess's reaction to his harp-playing shows that her own case is not essentially dissimilar. She, too, idealizes, and is far from seeing Angel for what he really is. Ian Gregor takes the point when he says that 'What is writ small in these paragraphs is writ large into her whole relationship with Angel Clare'.[9] The observation is also relevant to the part played by nature in the developing relationship. Tess's responses to the sights and sounds in the garden at this moment are a miniaturized version of Clare's responses to Talbothays. In either case, given what seems to the observer concerned a fitting human focus, a happy confusion of emotional and aesthetic reactions proves ripe for appropriation by romantic love.

My reservation about Gregor's account of the episode is that it puts the emphasis too particularly upon its relevance to Tess as an individual. Certainly many passages in Hardy do work in just this metaphorical way, with the landscape mirroring a character's state of mind or feeling. Here one could make out a case that the garden figures Tess's coarse earlier encounter with sexual passion and that the music played by Clare stands for the transformative new factor of idealizing love. But surely the diagnosis Hardy is proposing goes far beyond the particular relationship. His wider claim is that this is how human beings *in general* inevitably react. The garden scene is hyperbolic in that the social personalities of the lovers concerned are left entirely out of the account; but the hyperbole is designed to dramatize Hardy's point. Whatever the social situation might be we can escape neither from the insidious stirrings of animal instinct, nor from the need to cross-relate such stirrings with a miscellany of emotional and aesthetic responses. In a famous comment on Tess's tendency to interpret the sights and sounds of nature as a commentary on her plight, as 'part of her own story', Hardy states: 'Rather they became a part of it; for the world is only a psychological phenomenon, and what they seemed they were' (91). If, in the garden scene, 'The floating pollen seemed to be his notes made visible, and the dampness of the garden the weeping of the garden's sensibility', then, for Tess, this is what they *were*. All human lovers are liable to this kind of self-deception. We see what we project, and accordingly delude ourselves further.

In Hardy's work extremes of feeling are not rationally justified or resolved: they fold back upon themselves, or are deflected into some adjunctive experience. The process is summed up in the early poem 'Neutral Tones', which shows how the bitterness of a lovers' quarrel is intensified by the bleak setting in which it takes place yet how, by association, it infuses and makes more desolate that very setting. The elliptical idea produces an elliptical poem. Hardy's novels in general, and *Tess* in particular, feature many formulations of comparable reflexivity. The idea, and even the accompanying cadence, becomes familiar:

> They were as sublime as the moon and stars above them; and the moon and stars were as ardent as they. (69)

> ... the spirit of the scene, and of the moonlight, and of Nature, seemed harmoniously to mingle with the spirit of wine. (72)

> ... and the waves of colour mixed with the waves of sound. (128)

> So these two upper and nether visages confronted each other, all day long the white face looking down on the brown face, and the brown face looking up at the white face ... (277)

The landscape, the natural context, can prompt feelings, or reflect them, or corroborate them, or intensify them. It can elucidate only to the extent of suggesting that many of the impulses concerned are by no means exclusive to the human race.

If the quoted passage appears essentially confused (as Lodge claims) it is because Hardy sees sexual desire, love and human life at large as *being* confused and confusing. Things are what they seem – and that semblance may shift in a day, an hour, even a moment. So for him a novel must be 'an impression, not an argument'. At best it can only 'give shape and coherence to a series of seemings, or personal impressions...' (*Jude*, Preface). The debates he dramatizes are by definition inconclusive.

III

Against the stretch of water, where a school of mackerel twinkled in the afternoon light, was defined, in addition to the distant lighthouse, a church with its tower, standing about a quarter of a mile off, near the edge of the cliff. The churchyard gravestones could be seen in profile against the same vast spread of watery babble and unrest.

Among the graves moved the form of a man clothed in a white sheet, which the wind blew and flapped coldly every now and then. Near him moved six men bearing a long box, and two or three persons in black followed. The coffin, with its twelve legs, crawled across the isle, while around and beneath it the flashing lights from the sea and the school of mackerel were reflected; A fishing-boat, far out in the Channel, being momentarily discernible under the coffin also.

The procession wandered round to a particular corner, and halted, and paused there a long while in the wind, the sea behind them, the surplice of the priest still blowing. Jocelyn stood with his hat off: he was present, though he was a quarter of a mile off; and he seemed to hear the words that were being said, though nothing but the sea was audible. (*W-B*, II.–iii)

This is an extraordinary scene. Hearing of the death of his former sweetheart, Avice Caro, whom he has not so much as seen for twenty years, Pierston finds himself profoundly moved. On an impulse he hurries back from London to the Isle of Slingers to visit her grave. It so happens that he arrives in time to see her burial – but only from a great distance, as a detail within a panorama. This is one of Hardy's long-range scenes, like the final paragraphs of *Tess*, or the departure of the *Victory* in *The Trumpet-Major*, in which a relationship of love is abstracted to generality. If Pierston were at the graveside the experience would presumably be a personal one, reviving memories of Avice as an individual. It would probably also have a social element, as he met her surviving relatives. In the event Hardy gives us an impersonal, poeticized funeral, reduced to a multifarious tableau.

Yet unlike the passage from *Tess* discussed above this description is not flamboyantly written, seeming concerned chiefly with mere visual facts. Indeed in certain aspects – the grammar of the opening sentence, for example – it is arguably pedestrian at the stylistic level. What is intriguing about it is the mode of seeing, the perspective, the juxtapositions, the visual ironies. The responsive reader will want to follow the hints dropped by a novelist who sees and imagines so oddly and intensely.

In *The Well-Beloved* Hardy creates a specialized landscape of an uncharacteristic kind. As I have mentioned, the Isle of Slingers features but a single clump of trees, and seems virtually devoid of animal, bird or insect life. But this very sparseness allows the author a greater measure of schematic control. The simplified environment matches the simplified, even skeletal, story. Certain features of it are mention so frequently as to become motifs. These include the sea, the Race, the cliff, the quarries, the wind, the moon, the lighthouse, the lightship, the church and the castle. The quoted passage includes several of them in a very few lines. It is a strange exercise in surrealistic compression.

Hardy provides two clues as to how it should be read. Pierston, 'a quarter of a mile off' (the point is repeated) 'seems' to hear the words of the funeral service, though in point of fact nothing is audible but the sea. Though not present to his senses they are present to his mind. The same would hold true for some of the visual details of the panorama Hardy opens out to us. They could not all be seen, at any rate in these proportions and relationships, although they are theoretically available to be seen – available to the mind's eye. Certainly the reader can mentally view the episode on the basis of this super-saturated description, but the picture in the mind must be heightened and stylized. Hardy is deliberately going beyond the literal.

The other clue has come at the start of the chapter. Pierston has received word of Avice's death in the course of a fashionable London party, and almost immediately the sights before his eyes begin to give way to 'the vivid presentment of Avice Caro, and the old, old scenes on Isle Vindilia which were inseparable from her personality' (70). Hardy's account reads like a deliberate inversion of the final paragraphs of *Alice in Wonderland*. There the dream is decoded back into the literal; here the actuality gives way to the vision:

> The dining-room was real no more, dissolving under the bold stony promontory and the incoming West Sea. The handsome marchioness in geranium-red and diamonds…became one of the glowing vermilion sunsets that he had watched so many times over

Deadman's Bay, with the form of Avice in the foreground...The crannied features of the evergreen society lady...shaped themselves to the dusty quarries of his and Avice's parents...The ivy trailing about the table-cloth, the lights in the tall candlesticks, and the bunches of flowers, were transmuted into the ivies of the cliff-built Castle, the tufts of seaweed, and the lighthouses on the isle. (70)

All these details are inside Pierston's head, as features of a mental land-scape potentially more vivid than any actual prospect away from his native environment. Moroever they are closely linked to his suddenly-revived feeling for Avice. The ellipse is familiar: when he thinks of her he recalls the scenes they knew together; when he recalls those scenes he thinks of her.

For this reason it is appropriate that he participates in Avice's funeral only from a distance. His revived feeling for her is of a peculiarly abstract kind: 'it was love rarefied and refined to its highest attar' (73). To attend the funeral in the normal way would involve an irrelevant recollection of her social personality. His vantage-point a quarter of a mile from the actual churchyard enables him to take in a panorama full of sights and sounds which he links with his lost love – the sea, the wind, the cliff, a boat, the church, the lighthouse. Much that he can-not see, or can only glimpse, he can apprehend from earlier knowl-edge. Even before leaving London he has pictured the dead Avice, 'the moonlight irradiating her winding-sheet...reached only by the faint noises inherent in the isle; the tink-tink of the chisels in the quarries, the surging of the tides in the Bay, and the muffled grumbling of the currents in the never-pacified Race' (73). He loves her partly or largely for her associations with these things; he values these things partly or largely because they remind him of her. Roughly speaking he relates Avice to the Isle of Slingers as Clare relates Tess to Talbothays.

The garden scene in *Tess* carries forward a relationship: here the rela-tionship is over. It would seem that nothing is happening. The plot of *The Well-Beloved* could be identical if this description were excised. How, then, does it contribute to the overall economy of the novel? Its energy and singularity solicit attention: is that attention rewarded?

The episode resembles the one from *Tess* in several particulars. It concerns a single figure whose loved one is present only in an oblique sense. It concentrates intensely on what is seen and heard. The focus of attention is a funeral, but this scene also teems with activity, with oddity and with tensions – though here there is no 'equilibrium'. The sea is all 'babble and unrest', a school of fish – unlikely guests at a funeral – twinkle in the sunshine, lights are flashing, a wind is blowing. The disparate entities – oddly clad people, manmade objects, natural phenomena – are concatenated by diverse prepositions: 'against', 'in', 'with', 'above', 'near', 'across', 'around', 'beneath', 'behind', 'under'. Even the coffin contrives to crawl on its 'twelve legs'. Visually beneath it a fishing-boat suddenly appears – one kind of wooden box below another.

Any reader who has attended a burial will recognize this incongruous vitality and miscellaneous. As one tries to come to terms with the hard unvarying fact of the death of a loved person the contingent sights and sounds surrounding the funeral ceremony offer a counterpoint that may be variously experienced as distracting, ironic or consolatory. This confused sense of relevance is far from being a random response; rather it is an instinctive attempt to locate the death and the lost individual in the context of continuing, prolix, unresponsive life. Hardy's scene mimics the reactions of many a mourner, but does so on an operatic scale. As in ordinary life the essential reaction could be either positive or negative. A positive inner voice might claim: 'So many of the things she knew and loved seem to be participating in the ceremony'. A negative voice might whisper: 'How trifling the individual life seems in the midst of the mindless activities of Nature'.

At different times, and with equal conviction, Hardy will propose versions of both these views. Again and again he will represent one of his protagonists as a microscopic thing of no account – a speck, an ant, a fly. But 'the relative is all'. Soon after Pierston has fallen in love with the second Avice he happens to see her in the distance as 'a dot of a figure'; but to his imagination she is something very different:

> How incomparably the immaterial dream dwarfed the grandest of substantial things, when here, between those three sublimities – the sky, the rock, and the ocean – the minute personality of this washer-girl filled his consciousness to its extremest boundary, and the stupendous inanimate scene shrank to a corner therein. (102)

The funeral description implies yet another view. Essentially what Pierston is seeing *is* Avice. For him she had been a distillation of the life and the 'sublimities' before him, rather as Hardy's Proud Songster is a temporary coalescence of 'particles of grain,/And earth, and air, and rain'.

The movement and potential movement in the passage carry a further element of suggestion. The sea is restless, the wind blows, a garment flaps, the mackerel twinkle, the coffin walks: Avice may be dead, but Nature knows no punctuation points. As so often Hardy's juxtapositions imply progress or process. When in the *Life* he records seeing a ceme-tery behind the Montmartre can-can (240), or glimpsing through the bones of a skeleton a group of children dancing to a band (163), he is sardonically hinting future prospects. Here the coffin takes on incon-gruous life, but only the brief life of an insect. Soon it will be under ground. The twinkling mackerel, an image of multitudinous vitality, may well fall prey to the fishing-boat. It is not impossible that the boat itself may one day go down like that other wooden vessel, the coffin, which is momentarily aligned with it. Even the church on the cliff may eventually follow its predecessor over the edge.

The vivid, shifting, miscellaneous, cross-related, intriguing scene, like life itself, compels you, but defies you, to try to make sense of it. It puts human ideals and aspirations under scrutiny. Pierston watches the funeral still fired with his new-found fleshless passion, 'rarefied and refined', for the late Avice Caro. According to taste it could be seen as a source of cynicism or of optimism that that very evening he begins to fall in love with her daughter.

IV

At one's every step forward it rises higher against the south sky, with an obtrusive personality that compels the senses to regard it and consider. The eyes may bend in another direction, but never with-out the consciousness of its heavy, high-shouldered presence at its point of vantage. Across the intervening levels the gale races in a straight line from the fort, as if breathed out of it hitherward. With the shifting of the clouds the faces of the steeps vary in colour and in shade, broad lights appearing where mist and vagueness had pre-vailed, dissolving in their turn into melancholy gray, which spreads over and eclipses the luminous bluffs. In this so-thought immutable spectacle all is change.

Out of the invisible marine region on the other side birds soar suddenly into the air, and hang over the summits of the heights with the indifference of long familiarity. Their forms are white against the tawny concave of cloud, and the curves they exhibit in their floating signify that they are seagulls which have journeyed inland from expected stress of weather. As the birds rise behind the fort, so do the clouds rise behind the birds, almost, as it seems, stroking with their bagging bosoms the uppermost flyers.

The profile of the whole stupendous ruin, as seen at a distance of a mile eastward, is cleanly cut as that of a marble inlay. It is varied with protuberances, which from hereabouts have the animal aspect of warts, wens, knuckles, and hips. It may indeed be likened to an enormous many-limbed organism of an antediluvian time – partaking of the cephalopod in shape – lying lifeless, and covered with a thin green cloth, which hides its substance, while revealing its contour. This dull green mantle of herbage stretches down towards the levels, where the ploughs have essayed for centuries to creep up near and yet nearer to the base of the castle, but have always stopped short before reaching it. The furrows of these environing attempts show themselves distinctly, bending to the incline as they trench upon it; mounting in steeper curves, till the steepness baffles them, and their parallel threads show like the striae of waves pausing on the curl. The peculiar place of which these are some of the features is 'Mai-Dun', 'The Castle of the Great Hill', said to be the Dunium of Ptolemy, the capital of the Durotriges, which eventually came into Roman occupation, and was finally deserted on their withdrawal from the island.

'A Tryst at an Ancient Earthwork'

The story from which this extract is taken offers, in condensed form, a display of many of the essential descriptive and conceptual tendencies with which this book is concerned. To read it attentively is akin to turning up the bass to isolate the underlying rhythms of Hardy's art. This ancient earthwork is familiar territory for him: 'triple-ramparted Maidon' features several times in his fiction and poetry. Here he exploits it to the edge of self-indulgence.

The strangest aspect of this strangely intense passage is the fact that the intensity seems gratuitous. The scene concerned is not to be made the setting for a tragic denouement nor is it a metaphor for some striking human drama soon to unfold. 'A Tryst at an Ancient Earthwork' is little more than a sketch or fragment, featuring a great deal more Earthwork than Tryst. To be more precise, such plot as there is takes up little more than the final third of the narrative. Nor does the story, *qua* story, require elaborate contextualization: any old dark night would suffice for what occurs. The hyperbolic description seems to be there for its own sake. Hardy quite often borrowed strong passages from his occasional work for serious duty in his novels. So, for example, paragraphs from 'The Dorsetshire Labourer' and his review of William Barnes's poetry do useful work in *Tess* and *The Mayor of Casterbridge*.[10] It would have been no surprise if vivid elements of 'A Tryst at an Ancient Earthwork' had been similarly recycled, for the setting and its associations bear on some of his deepest interests. But in the event it stands alone: a bravura exercise, a florid and striking concert aria.

The episode in question could very well constitute a chapter in a Hardy novel: in fact the appointment of Henchard and Susan at the Ring comes close to it. In both cases the initial point stressed, even laboured, is the discrepancy between the brevity of the meeting and the unimaginable longevity of the meeting place. Both passages hark back to the Jotuns. But the encounter in *The Mayor of Casterbridge* constitutes a crucial step in the carefully chronicled 'story of a man of character'. 'Earthwork' is not part of anything. Present tense narration underlines the transience of the episode: for storyteller and reader it is happening *now*. The slight action leads nowhere. The two characters, one of them a virtual spectator, are not even given names. If any sort of 'meaning' is to be derived from the work it surely originates in description rather than story.

Hardy stakes out a huge landscape. The meeting-place – 'this largest Ancient-British work in the kingdom' (646) – is first viewed from 'a distance of a mile'. Somewhere far behind it is the 'invisible marine region' from which the seagulls have appeared. The temporary apex of a gigantic triangle is the 'tawny concave of cloud' above the birds – which is later dispersed to reveal the moon. Not content with this species of magnitude Hardy enlarges it with incommensurates, 'adding its age to its size, and its size to its solitude' (646). The scene he is describing and evoking occupies an enormous, undefinable, four-dimensional space.

An inherent contrast or conflict, a kind of dialectic, is implied throughout the opening description and further developed as the story goes on. On the one hand there is a constant emphasis on the massiveness and antiquity of the fort; on the other there is a dramatization of what it to become a ferocious assault by the elements. The seagulls have arrived only just ahead of the storm they are fleeing from:

> The wind, quickening, abandons the natural direction it has pursued on the open upland, and takes the course of the gorge's length, rushing along therein helter-skelter, and carrying thick rain upon its back. The rain is followed by hailstones which fly through the defile in battalions – rolling, hopping, ricochetting, snapping, clattering down the shelving banks in an undefinable haze of confusion. (647)

The military metaphor implied in 'battalions' and 'ricochetting' appropriately suggests that the fortress has been subjected to sudden attack. A little later the storm is said to travel round the castle 'like a circumambulating column of infantry'. But the opening description has in any case made it clear that Mai-Dun is permanently beleaguered. As wind, rain or hail assail it from the air, there are further attacks at ground level. The furrows of the ploughmen rise higher and higher, like slow-moving waves, 'trenching upon' the slopes. There are many references in the story to forgotten battles fought in and around the fortification. These come to seem mere types of the endless conflict between the earthwork and the elements.

An initial impression might be that the story provides a typical Hardy picture of erosion – erosion on the grand scale, depicted in terms of a battle. The age and presence of the 'stupendous ruin' may defy the encroaching forces but it must ultimately fall. Indeed the buildings which once stood upon the site have long been shattered, laid low and dispersed. Only the earthwork itself remains to defy its attackers. The scale of the siege dramatizes the greatness of the powers on either side. Mighty are the powers that tirelessly fret and batter and imperceptibly dissolve this colossal earthwork. Awesome is the fortress that has withstood such an onslaught for centuries, maintaining its 'heavy, high-shouldered presence'. The essential theme of the tale, it might be claimed, is this ceaseless natural war. On this reading the illegal activities of the antiquarian are simply an excuse for a Hardy set-piece in his most extravagant manner. If the story were a painting the human figures would be tiny, irrelevant intruders in an overpowering landscape.

But a different kind of reading is suggested by the narrator's musings about the origins of the fort. He claims that the idea must have derived from 'some remote mind capable of prospective reasoning to a far extent':

> Who was the man that said, 'Let it be built here!'...Whether he were some great one of the Belgae, or of the Durotriges, or the travelling engineer of Britain's united tribes, must for ever remain time's secret; his form cannot be realized, nor his countenance, nor the tongue that he spoke, when he set down his foot with a thud and said, 'Let it be here!' (650)

As tone and language imply, this 'remote' figure effectively does duty for God. By his fiat a world was created. 'A Tryst at an Ancient Earthwork' offers an account of the workings of that miniature world and, by extension, of the workings of the world at large.

The central factor is ceaseless movement. The key sentence of the opening paragraphs quoted above is the ultra-Hardyesque 'In this so-thought immutable spectacle all is change'. Certainly 'the gale races', clouds shift, light dissolves, 'birds soar'; but there is something beyond such motions – a structural dynamic. One descriptive frame of reference collapses, or melts, into another. The speeding wind shifts the cloud, which breaks to produce a change in the light. The gulls fleeing the storm reach a frozen inland sea of 'mounting' furrows. The earthwork itself, 'an enormous many-limbed organism', has 'an animal aspect of warts, wens, knuckles and hips'. The gale seems to have been 'breathed out of it'. We learn that this monster 'rises...against the south sky' well before we are told that 'as the birds rise behind the fort, so do the clouds rise behind the birds'. The vegetation seems to have a motion of its own, independent of the wind: 'The dead heads of these various grasses – fescues, fox-tails, and ryes – bob and twitch as if pulled by a string underground' (647).

This diversity of movement duly generates a diversity of sounds. Even when the fort has 'ceased to be visible' it somehow 'asserts its existence behind the night gauzes as persistently as if it had a voice' (646). The twitching plants are audible: 'From a few thistles a whistling proceeds; and even the moss speaks, in its humble way, under the stress of the blast' (647). At the other end of the scale a fresh wind 'from a new quarter' produces a sound from the fort as a whole 'playing upon it bodily as upon a harp' (647). Later, amid 'the roar of the storm' 'a rumbling as from its subterranean vaults – if there are any – fills the castle' (648).

By this stage the reader's 'realistic' impressions of the fortress have surely become twisted and deformed. At first too far away to be seen in any detail 'It is now so enlarged by nearness that its whole shape cannot be taken in at one view' (646). The fanciful account of the voices it produces is a way of asserting that the earthwork exceeds our imaginative capacities as its largest and smallest sounds defy the limitations of our hearing. None the less 'Acoustic perceptions multiply tonight'. Imagination can make good the deficiencies of the senses. If, with our mind's ear, we can detect the ghostly utterances of the moss, then by extension we might somehow apprehend the 'strange articulations' within the now non-existent gateway: 'the lingering air-borne vibrations of conversations uttered at least fifteen hundred years ago' (648–9).

Hardy effects a transition from these acoustic abstractions, these 'nebulous imaginings', by the distraction of 'a real moving of something close at hand'. What the narrator sees calls for comment:

It is but the heaving of a mole who chooses such weather as this to work in from some instinct that there will be nobody abroad to molest him. As the fine earth lifts and lifts and falls loosely aside fragments of burnt clay roll out of it – clay that once formed part of cups or other vessels used by the inhabitants of the fortress. (649)

Since the brisk archaeological paw-work of the mole is rendered visible to the narrator by the lightning-flashes, which by now conveniently happen to be 'sheet-like and nearly continuous', the claimed reversion to realism is less than convincing. The activities of the mole are 'there', very much in the same sense that the voice of the moss is 'there', as a deducible 'fact' not normally to be perceived. Hardy is sacrificing conventional realism to plenitude. As often, he chooses to represent as physically apprehensible a combination of effects so minute and various that their co-presence could be registered only theoretically. He uses the former approach to procure the latter awareness.

'A Tryst at an Ancient Earthwork' is a lattice-work of echoes and correspondences. The wind plays upon the whole fortification 'as upon a harp'. A page or two later the narrator reflects that 'harps have probably twanged more or less tuneful notes' (650) within the central enclosure. The movement and the colour of the lightning remind him of the swords once wielded by the soldiery. The miniature 'heaving' of the mole recalls the 'heave of the whole atmosphere' which preceded the storm. It throws up a mound 'At first no larger than a man's fist'. Earlier the ramparts of the fortification have been described as overlapping each other 'like loosely clasped fingers' (648). When the narrator's friend, the archaeologist, eventually arrives his appearance is a reminder of the unseen mole: 'He is entirely in black broadcloth – or rather, at present, black and brown, for he is bespattered with mud from his heels to the crown of his low hat' (651). His first quoted words – 'Nobody to interrupt us at this time of night!' – articulate the 'instinct' of the mole.

Essentially these nocturnal diggers are doing the same thing, if for very different purposes – burrowing in the earth and uncovering the remains of artefacts centuries old. The mole is not the only wild creature that digs among the remains. There have been earlier references to 'a few wild badgers, rabbits, and hares'. The antiquarian's eyes 'shine like those of a lynx' (651). As he warms to his task he sometimes 'falls on his knees, burrowing with his hands in the manner of a hare' (652). Along with the other animals he belongs to the forces assailing the earthwork. After century upon century of attrition 'Nothing is left visible that the hands can seize on or the weather overturn' (650): but these invaders are cutting into the very substance of the fortification. The antiquarian wields his pick with vigour, and on reaching the level he seeks 'draws the implement out as feelingly as if it had entered a man's body' (652). The narrator and his friend are time-travellers: 'we have lowered ourselves into an ancient world' (652). A warning notice-board provides the sole reminder 'that the time is really the nineteenth century' (649). Even when the storm recommences 'My companion digs on unconcernedly; he is living two thousand years ago, and despises things of the moment as dreams'(653). He wipes his forehead with the same handkerchief with which he has just wiped a Roman skull.

The earlier fancies of the narrator become realities of a sort, as his pertinacious friend successively unearths a mosaic, a bottle, a fragment of a weapon, the complete skeleton of a fallen warrior and a bronze-gilt image of Mercury. What has been imagined is now seen – but only for a short time. The artefacts are 'inhumed' – save for the statuette, which is furtively purloined – and the skeleton disintegrates on contact with the air.

The circularity of 'inhumation' is the ultimate theme of the story. In a sense the conflict which has been repeatedly invoked proves scarcely to be a conflict at all. However the earthwork is assailed it dissolves back into itself. Roman tiles and pots have been made from the earth and duly revert to it. The combatants have been physically absorbed by the land on which they fought. Hardy sketches a comparable idea diagrammatically in his illustration to 'Her Dilemma', in *Wessex Poems*. We see, in cross section, the dying man, in church with his lover, while below ground level lurk the coffins or the scattered bones of generations of earlier unfortunates.

At the end of 'Tryst' the main theme is recapitulated in a brief coda. Seven years have passed and the antiquarian has himself died, presumably to be reabsorbed in his turn by the terrain he once explored. The story has led nowhere, has looped back upon itself. In a *reductio ad absurdum* of Hardy's descriptive art the description has swallowed the narrative. Alternatively the doings which constitute that narrative are seen to be no more than specialized examples of the processes continually at work in the scene described. The small depredations of the scholarly antiquarian come to seem of little more consequence than those of the heedless mole.

The very first sentence of 'A Tryst at an Ancient Earthwork' announces that the 'obtrusive personality' of the fortification 'compels the senses to regard it and consider'. It is a curious and revealing formulation. The earthwork is present in powerfully sensual terms: sight, hearing and touch are vividly addressed. But those first reactions have the effect of precipitating thought. Sensually involved we reflect on the meaning of this strange and overwhelming phenomenon – or rather the story reflects on our behalf. Hardy's 'consideration' shows the earthwork and the larger world which it figures to be in a state of permanent conflict, motion, change, dissolution, reabsorption and redefinition. The most ambitious of human projects, the saddest of human tragedies, recapitulate these processes while forming part of them.

7
'This insubstantial pageant'

The argument of this book has entailed oscillation between minute particularities and large abstractions. My aim has been to show how much of the essential energy of a Hardy novel is to be found in the descriptive detail, especially in his depiction of landscape, and indeed to assert that this energy is so strong as to encroach upon, destabilize or even assimilate the story it ostensibly subserves. 'Orthodox' criticism often takes a step or two in this direction – for example, when considering scenes of solitude: Tess listening in the garden, Clym working on the heath, Giles shrouding a tree, Knight hanging from a cliff. There is general acknowledgement that background can bear on characterization. But it is a long way from that position to the more radical one proposed here. This final chapter will recapitulate the case I have been trying to make, and will show that the suggested approach is not hostile to more familiar interpretations of Hardy; rather it offers to incorporate them in a revised mode of reading.

II

A novelist with what Hardy called 'idiosyncrasy of regard' may be radically revalued as that idiosyncrasy, perhaps only incidentally acknowledged by early critics, comes to be more fully appreciated and more sympathetically interpreted. Dickens is a case in point. His detailed, stylized, often hyperbolic descriptions of clothes or meals or gestures were enjoyed from the first for their oddity and vividness, but were long perceived as exotic and dispensable extras. Orwell, a great admirer of Dickens, suggested something of the sort when praising his 'wonderful gargoyles' while deploring the shoddiness of his 'architecture'.[1] The dramatic rise in Dickens's reputation, roughly over the past forty years,

has derived largely from the realization that these apparently gratuitous passages are in fact diversely functional – for example, in terms of
social definition, of displaying mental or psychological states, of contributing to a variety of metaphorical patterns. Effectively they are
indeed elements in a coherent novelistic architecture of Dickens's own
devising. When so understood they take on a new depths of meaning,
and the works concerned come to be redefined in terms of form and
strategy. In the process traditional notions of fictional 'architecture' are
themselves redefined. The genre is amplified.

A roughly similar process of reappraisal has been developing in relation to Hardy's use of 'background'. It was obvious to his original audience that his work was full of passages of poetic natural description,
notable in their own right yet having a bearing upon the story being
told. At the circumstantial level an emphasis on terrain, season and
weather was plainly appropriate to tales of country life and farm work.
At the thematic level the scale and seeming permanence of the landscape stressed the littleness of man's doings and the brevity of his life.
The indifference of nature suggested the indifference of fate. In the
spirit of pathetic fallacy weather or scenery could seem to respond to
human moods, as when the idyllic summer at Talbothays reflects and
enhances the growing love between Tess and Angel. Such devices were
immediately recognizable, familiar from long tradition.

The 'background' descriptions acquired further status when it was
recognized that they could serve at least two more purposes. One was
to provide an opportunity for metaphorical comment on particular
aspects of the narrative. So (to take notorious examples) the washing
away of the flowers Troy plants on Fanny's grave suggests the shallow-
ness and transience of his repentance; Jude's killing of a trapped rabbit
and Tess's destruction of the wounded pheasants draw attention to
their own status as victims of the cruelties of mankind. This mode of
symbolic commentary, of course, was to become an essential working
method for D. H. Lawrence and others. As an accepted Modernist practice it hardly calls for further comment here.

More recent, and more complex, have been the accounts of Hardy
which see his landscape descriptions providing expression, through
displacement, of a character's temperament or mood. One example,
discussed in an earlier chapter, is the frozen landscape which confronts
Boldwood the morning after his receipt of Bathsheba's valentine –
a scene which displays by means of visual analogy his emotional
and psychological confusion. Appreciation of the extent and the sub-
tlety of Hardy's use of this technique precludes any notion that his

characterization is simple or shallow. His metaphorical commentaries show a poetic suggestiveness and ambiguity which powerfully dramatize feeling while conceding, through their obliquity, a respectful margin of indeterminacy. Seen in this light background description becomes a vital adjunct to characterization.

In this book I have been proposing several further ways, some of them more radical, in which story and description interpenetrate. The metaphors so far mentioned in this chapter are special cases, in that Hardy uses them to make some particular local point. Much more generally his backgrounds provide him with an enormous store-house of comparisons across category. The hill of Portland resembles a whale, a star can flutter like a bird, water can cluck like a hen. Preponderantly such associations are invoked to link human beings with the natural world. Tess, for example, can be likened to a fly, a cat, a snake, a flower, a mushroom. The recurrence of such similes is curiously diverse in its effects. It encourages a version of the synaesthetic response, a sense of the relationship between one kind of aesthetic experience and another. It suggests shared attributes: a mushroom has the tender skin of a girl; a wasp can get drunk, as a man can; ivy clings to the host tree like a weak wife to her husband; a rhubarb-leaf can wilt in hot sunshine like an elderly woman. With so much in common, human, animal and vegetable life cannot be seen as neatly separable. Hardy is insisting that we are all members of the family of living things.

The inference must be that man is not at the centre of the system of metaphor which nature provides. Consciousness is the sole factor which differentiates the clinging human wife from the ivy-wife. Our stories, even our tragedies, are merely special instances of the general plight. Hardy's landscapes are prolific in potential dramas of which Man's story is only one. Stars and moon, heath and woodland, sea and stream, and their inhabitants, if any, are alive in their own ways, susceptible to change, conflict and depredation. The human tragedies in which Hardy absorbs us are versions both of smaller dramas – the death of an animal, an insect, a tree – and of larger ones – the decline of a civilization, the destruction of a species. We are environed with fellow-sufferers. Hardy spells out the idea in 'The Wind Blew Words':

> The wind blew words along the skies,
>   And these it blew to me
> Through the wide dusk: 'Lift up your eyes,
>   Behold this troubled tree,
> Complaining as it sways and plies;

It is a limb of thee.
'Yea, too, the creatures sheltering round –
Dumb figures, wild and tame...'

In a letter written in 1910 to the Secretary of the Humanitarian League Hardy develops this idea, suggesting that Darwin's *On the Origin of Species* implied the need for 'a re-adjustment of altruistic morals' to take in 'the whole animal kingdom': 'While man was deemed to be a creation apart from all other creations, a secondary or tertiary morality was considered good enough towards the "inferior" races; but no person who reasons nowadays can escape the trying conclusion that this is not maintainable' (*Life*, 376–7).

Because he sees us as a species like other species, Hardy instinctively creates landscapes dense with latent analogy. They constitute not background but explanatory context. They must be 'read', as the stories of the human characters are read, if his vision is to be properly understood.

In novel after novel, poem after poem Hardy displays and comments on the brevity and insignificance of human life. It is his habit to portray individuals as (a favourite word) 'specks'. In his first novel he has Manston observe on his behalf: 'When we survey the long race of men, it is strange and still more strange to find that they are mainly dead men, who have scarcely ever been otherwise' (*DR*, 407). Nearly half a century later he remarks of *Moments of Vision*: 'I do not expect much notice will be taken of these poems: they mortify the human sense of self-importance by showing, or suggesting, that human beings are of no matter or appreciable value in this nonchalant universe' (*Life*, 408–9). It's well known, of course, that Hardy made a number of particular observations of this kind. What I am further proposing is that the same apparently reductive view is implicit in his very habit of seeing and describing. The Hardy 'vision' would seem to proclaim, among other messages, that we don't matter.

Many admirers of Hardy have tended to feel a resistance to even the simpler version of this line of argument. My expanded claim must at first glance look suspiciously like a Pyrrhic tribute, even if it is in line with Hardy's own claims. The 'larger' vision proposed would seem to call in question the status of narrative and characterization, the very elements which have drawn generations of ordinary readers to his fiction. What remains of a given novel if 'story' is dissolved into nullity by Darwinian acids? Why poignantly evoke the individuality of a man doomed to die early if the subtext is implying that he is of no more account, in the wider scheme of things, than a felled tree? But the issue need not be – should not be – thought of in terms of simple opposition, 'story' versus 'vision'. What is called for is a modification of response, a move towards the kind of reciprocal reading which seems natural in the case of landscape painting, and which finds a kind of equilibrium in a system of mutually qualifying instabilities.

III

Although 'The Leaping Horse' has inescapably the stasis of paint on canvas it is essentially concerned – to use Constable's own word – with 'bustle'. Trees and clouds are swept by the wind, a barge travels along moving water, men are at work, the barge-horse is in mid-leap, and a startled moorhen darts off. In showing the scene as it is Constable suggests how it is changing. But Leslie Parris and Ian Fleming-Williams remind us that there are further sensory possibilities in Constable's paintings: 'For him landscape was a total experience – aural and tactile as well as visual – and if we are to read him aright, and fully, we should be on the lookout for evocations of sound'.[2] At this level, too, there is action and reaction in the work. Comfortable amid the noises of wind and water the moorhen will have been startled by the clatter of the horse's hooves, and will be shrieking as it flies away.

Through such sleights Constable crams more into his painting than it can hold in literal terms – movement, sound, interaction, time. His finished works often, as in this case, have even a kind of formal plurality, being a distillation or superimposition of a number of sketches or studies. The apparent realism goes beyond realism.

Hardy, as we have seen, works in a comparable way. In describing landscape he, too, is rarely content with showing simply what is 'there'. Hints of damage or decay can imply something of the past and the future of a tree, a house, even a cliff. An emphasis on changing light or weather can suggest the volatility of the presented scene: in an hour, a minute, a moment it may appear quite otherwise. In many cases, as has been suggested, Hardy achieves an effect of super-saturation by describing more phenomena than a real-life spectator or auditor could possibly take in at once – a skyscape of stars, an expanse of minute flowers or mosses, subterranean stirrings, sounds beyond the compass of the human ear. Many of his characters project their sight with telescopes, and are suddenly at close quarters with something far away. In a passage from the *Life*, previously quoted, Hardy imagines the insects around him 'magnified by the microscope: creatures like elephants, flying dragons etc' (110). Many of his own descriptions of ants, wasps or gnats have just such a magnifying effect. The focal length shifts, and we are eye to eye with some small creature, like Knight with his trilobite. Frequently – if not, indeed, almost inevitably – such apparent intimacy of observation is no more than inferential, as when Hardy refers to thrushes and blackbirds singing 'with such modulation that you seem to see their little tongues curl inside their bills in their emphasis' (*Life*, 117). Expanding and contracting perspectives convey a vertiginous plenitude and density. In magnitude, in littleness, in sound, in activity, the given scene exceeds human capacities of response.

In their different ways, then, both Constable and Hardy are displaying overspill, excess. The 'scene' ostensibly shown reaches beyond its apparent limits. More is revealed or implied than the form can contain. What such a technique suggests is that received ideas of 'a view' or 'a landscape' can be no more than matters of convention. Nature's pluralities everywhere mock the feebleness of human perception, and are everywhere in process of change. The *Well-Beloved* funeral, for example, freezes a concatenation of transitions, catching shifting, miscellaneous forms in a momentary pattern, instantly to dissolve. Constable's scene is similarly momentary: the moorhen is disappearing, the leaping horse will descend, the barge will pass on, the clouds shift and leaves begin to fall in the wind.

The emphasis on these larger energies and rhythms cannot but modify one's response to whatever human story is being sketched. It is not merely that Constable's bargemen are moving away like the horse or the moorhen, not merely that Pierston and Avice's other mourners seem as transient as the twinkling mackerel. In either case we are made to see that our construction of a drama, or scene, is merely that – not 'reality' but an arbitrary, perhaps momentary, concentration on a few phenomena selected from a myriad.

Andrew Graham-Dixon, whose comments about the sense of tumult and struggle in *The Leaping Horse* were quoted earlier, would seem to have a consistent interest in suggestions of movement, change or dissolution in graphic art in general. He praises the way in which the restlessness of the mobile reflects the idea that 'Even the most substantial objects are microscopically and sub-microscopically mobile: matter itself is volatile'.[3] More surprisingly he finds constant movement in the apparently tranquil still-life paintings of Morandi, claiming that in his work 'Objects lose their individuality and become part of a continuum of change'.[4] This effect is achieved by a variety of means, for example the suggestion of analogy between objects very different in scale – such that wine-carafes can resemble houses – or the painter's wavering brushstroke which conveys a sense 'that things really are as fluid and unfixed as his images of them'. The conclusion is that 'Morandi's world is not still, but forever in motion'. In the same spirit Graham-Dixon praises the sculptures of Medardo Rosso as being 'true to the mobile, fluctuant nature of experience: true to the fact that no one and nothing ever looks the same twice'.[5] A characteristic work by Rosso will present 'the likeness of a human being preserved but vulnerably so, on the brink of melting back and away into the nothing from which it came'.

Clearly art of this kind defies the ideal of iconic summation. It burgeons, secretes, shifts, effervesces, unravels. Programmed into it is a sense of change, provisionality, incompleteness. We are presented with scenes or objects virtually self-cancelling. The true 'subject' is rather the continuing life-processes which in their very transience they momentarily illustrate. In projecting the ceaseless, sustaining energies of existence the artist undermines the existential autonomy of the person or object apparently selected to represent them. The scenes displayed are delusive, ambiguous, evanescent, reflecting the dubieties and complexities of our habitual ways of seeing and conceptualizing.

In the preceding chapters I have been trying to show that Hardy's art works very much in this way. The buildings he describes are repeatedly seen to be in slow dissolution, leaning, cracking, rotting. His heroines age before our eyes, already 'worn' at thirty. His 'proud songsters' – finches, thrushes and nightingales – are temporary assemblages of chemicals. Any of his protagonists can be seen as one of a 'long line', stretching back into prehistory, of essentially identical figures. Their ardours are no more than manifestations of the vitality of nature at large, aspirations to survive, to be happy, to breed or to overcome – aspirations they share with ant or gnat.

From this point of view the stories Hardy tells profess the barest local and temporary significance. They can be no more than episodes, shaped and comprehended by our species alone, instantly to be swallowed up by time and space. Narrative foreground dissolves into existential background.

IV

Mutability, transience, the brevity of human life: these are among the ancient themes of art. Human hopes, achievements and pretensions, the poet laments, will ultimately be as nothing. Love fades like the morning dew. Regal power is as frail: Shelley shows the remains of the colossal statue of Ozymandias dissolving into desert sand. After posing the question 'What are the hopes of man?' Byron puts a similar case more flippantly, but reaches a similar conclusion:

> Let not a monument give you or me hopes,
> Since not a pinch of dust remains of Cheops.
> (*Don Juan* I, CCXIX)

Tennyson's 'In Memoriam' proposes a larger view of mutability, very close to the one I am attributing to Hardy:

> The hills are shadows, and they flow
> From form to form, and nothing stands;
> They melt like mist, the solid lands,
> Like clouds they shape themselves and go.
> (123, ll. 5ff.)

For Tennyson, as for many another poet, such a vision of the workings of the world is conducive to despair. If 'nothing stands', where are meaning and purpose to be found?

Often in art this question seems to be posed as a conceptual last word. We live in the shadow of dissolution and approaching nescience: what more is there to say? It wouldn't be difficult to show that Hardy himself regularly proposes just such a view. But there is, of course, as he will then proceed to demonstrate, a great deal more to say. At the frontier between life and annihilation many transactions remain feasible. We bring into play – may even have thrust upon us – a variety of recuperative paradoxes and stratagems. Hardy, who spends so much time at or near this frontier is typically idiosyncratic, oblique and downright self-contradictory in his choice and deployment of such responses. It is their complexity and reflexivity which gives his novels that elusive, shifting coloration, as of shot silk.

Even setting aside the consolations of organized religion there are counter-moves, long familiar in art, in the war against evanescence. One or two were mentioned in the chapter on erosion. Poets have often felt wonder in contemplating the very process of change, or the life-force that produces it. Man does not, after all, vanish into nothingness: he is re-formed – like everything else in creation. The seemingly changeless impassivity of Egdon Heath or of the Cliff With No Name is delusive. They, too, will 'melt like mist'. Is there not something awe-inspiring in this very universality of change? Wordsworth, to quote an obvious example, celebrates the 'motion', the 'force', that he feels infusing the whole of creation, including 'the mind of man'. In 'Tintern Abbey' he writes of those moments of spiritual insight when

> ... the breath of this corporeal frame,
> And even the motion of our human blood
> Almost suspended, we are laid asleep
> In body, and become a living soul ... (ll. 44–7)

The implication is that the loss of 'corporeal' individuality is a necessary and small price to pay for the higher state of absorption in the 'continuum of change'.

Hardy, of course, often gestures towards such an abstract life-principle, beyond human consciousness or particular physical manifestations. Only rarely, however, does he seem to find anything consolatory in the idea. It seems relevant that as a young man he repeatedly marked in the Bible the passage from the First Book of Kings describing Elijah's experience of God's voice[6]:

> And he said, Go forth and stand upon the mount before the Lord. And behold, the Lord passed by, and a great and strong wind rent the mountains, and brake in pieces the rocks before the Lord; but the Lord was not in the wind: and after the wind an earthquake; but the Lord was not in the earthquake: And after the earthquake a fire; but the Lord was not in the fire: and after the fire a still small voice. (*First Book of Kings*, ch. 19)

Ultimately, however, such abstractions, such reachings towards an underlying principle of creation, seem to afford Hardy little succour. As Hillis Miller rightly observes: 'His nature is matter moved by an impersonal, unthinking energy, and in this it is quite unlike the nature of Coleridge, Wordsworth or Hopkins'.[7] The power which Wordsworth finds divine Hardy feels to be aimless. It is true that in *The Dynasts* he proposes the possibility that what he calls 'the Immanent Will' may evolve in the direction of consciousness and creativity (e.g. the final Chorus, p. 525), but this is not a hope which he explores in depth or develops elsewhere. Characteristically he represents the Will as blind energy, active to no end.

To acknowledge so much, however, is by no means to close the case. This may be Hardy's philosophical position, in so far as he can be said to have one, but the belief does not inform his habitual mode of vision. The comparison with Constable again seems relevant. As we look at *The Leaping Horse* an immediate and basic reaction is surely exhilaration at its suffusing energy – an energy of which, it seems, the painter's own creative vigour is an extension. Whether or not Hardy is 'ultimately' pessimistic, it is undeniable that scene after scene in his work conveys a sense of invigoration. Obviously there is many a set-piece episode of ferocious storm or glorious sunshine in which a protagonist is stirred to dramatic action or instinctive happiness; but even at the quiet end of the descriptive spectrum Hardy shows how everyday natural energies can rally the spirits. As we have seen, the sights and sounds of the dawning day rouse Bathsheba from despair; the frolickings of tiny creatures in a water-butt reanimate Manston's energies. Hardy several times, in a variety of formulations, acknowledges what he calls (*Tess*, 109) 'The irresistible, universal, automatic tendency to find sweet pleasure somewhere, which pervades all life, from the meanest to the highest...'. Locally his work is often celebratory, suggesting not merely that man can participate in the exuberant energies of nature, but that he cannot help doing so, that he is subject to them. 'Motion' – or 'Will' – may ultimately lead nowhere, but in the short term it can still startle us into happiness.

An earlier chapter offered preliminary comment on Hardy's acknowledgement of possible afterlives. He does have occasional recourse to familiar poetic consolations, including those famously enunciated in the great odes of Shelley and Keats. One claim these poets repeatedly make is that although the individual must die, the type will survive. There will be other springs, other autumns, other lovers. The song of the lark or the nightingale has been heard and will be heard through untold generations. A second affirmation is that in any case transient beauty may be preserved in art, as in the 'cold pastoral' of the Grecian Urn. In this latter spirit Hardy appropriately rejoices that through 'Shelley's Skylark' one particular song-bird has been 'made immortal', but he is too modest ever to claim to be immortalizing something on his own account. Indeed many of his poems have an extra charge of poignancy as seeming to assume that the memory they recapture is utterly personal to their author, and on that account all too mortal.

On a number of occasions he contemplates heredity as one manifestation of the survival of the type: 'The eternal thing in man,/That heeds no call to die' ('Heredity'). The distinctive beauty of Avice Caro is reiterated in her daughter and granddaughter. In *A Laodicean* Somerset reflects on the survival of the characteristic De Stancy nose through generation after generation. Learning of Elizabeth-Jane's true parentage Henchard studies her as she lies in her bed:

In sleep there come to the surface buried genealogical facts, ancestral curves, dead men's traits, which the mobility of daytime animation screens and overwhelms. In the present statuesque repose of the young girl's countenance Richard Newson's was unmistakably reflected. (*MC*, 126)

Hardy often shows himself intrigued by such patterns of recurrence, but it is to be doubted whether his interest goes much deeper. Elizabeth-Jane's lineage may be disclosed when she sleeps, but when she wakes it is 'the mobility of daytime animation' that makes her the person she is, and 'overwhelms' the 'dead men's traits'. It seems unlikely that the Cytherea who speaks of 'my single opportunity of existence' or the Tess who hates the thought of being 'one of a long row only', would find solace either in the survival of 'the family face' or in the reflection that this year's 'instalment' of birds and flowers will be succeeded by another and another. What is Process (they seem specifically to ask) in isolation from the thinking, feeling individuals who express it and perceive it? To Hardy himself the answer might nonetheless be: 'at least something'. Sometimes the idea of the 'long row' is presented in a positive light, conveying a sense of healthy continuity and shared tradition, as in the description of the medieval barn in *Far from the Madding Crowd*. On an alternative track, if Shelley's skylark and his own 'proud songsters' melt back into the landscape, some element of their existence is preserved in the precipitation of new living forms. The poems 'Transformations' (earlier quoted) and 'Voices from Things Growing in a Churchyard' seem to find some tranquillity in the thought that the bodies of the dead may be transmuted into living leaves and flowers, stirring in the breeze. That this is no casual conceit is made clear by its prominence in the final stanza of 'Rain on a Grave', one of the poems written in the aftermath of Emma's death:

> Soon will be growing
>   Green blades from her mound,
> And daisies be showing
>   Like stars on the ground,
> Till she form part of them –
> Ay – the sweet heart of them,

> Loved beyond measure
> With a child's pleasure
> All her life's round.

Here the idea is positively consolatory, the green blades, the daisies, the stars and the child-like aspect of Emma mutually assimilated in an impression of a diffused innocence and beauty.

The general position would seem to be that although in absolute terms Hardy's view of 'motion' or 'the life-force' or 'the Immanent Will' is a pessimistic one, the series of seemings which constitute his view of life includes local antidotes, local glimpses of compensation. It has often been remarked that the general 'pessimism' of his work is piquantly counterpointed by effusions of energy and joy. As Gillian Beer puts it: 'we enter his works not only to be chagrined and thwarted, but also sustained by the moment-by-moment plenitude of experience offered us.'[8] She adds, in a brilliantly apposite phrase, that the reader of a Hardy novel retains almost to the last 'a passionate sense of possible happiness'.

There is a related positive impulse which again links Hardy to the graphic artists mentioned in this chapter. The sculptor who captures a fleeting human face, or the painter who freezes a changing landscape, has retrieved something from the flux of experience. He may concede or even proclaim that the retrieval is temporary: there need be no implication of semi-permanence as in the case of the Grecian Urn. The perishability of the work of art itself may be implied in the highlighted perishability of the presented subject. It could be said of Rosso, for example, that his work snatches from oblivion a human countenance, or at least a particular perception of that countenance, just as 'The Leaping Horse' dramatically freezes a multiplicity of natural activities: this is what is seen NOW. Mere attempts in this kind, even when professedly evanescent on their own account, could be seen as implying a tribute to the singularity of our species. What the artist is attempting is no more than a special application of a universal human response. As time flows and worlds change we, uniquely, are the shapers, the meaning-makers, discerning patterns amid the flux and preserving them for contemplation at least a little longer. Where such a 'pattern' is found amid the quieter registers of experience – a Cornfield, a Woman Reading a Letter – another kind of assertion is implicit: that we are not overwhelmed or even intimidated by mere scale. We see the universe on our own terms, make our own values and shape our lives by our own rules. If it is true that these perceptions and inventions are subjective, arbitrary, artificial, they are not chaotically miscellaneous, but part of a common human heritage. They have coherence and continuity; they are communicable. If they seem a fragile structure as against the annihilating forces of time and nescience this very fragility has the shaped, containing delicacy and beauty of an eggshell.

Hardy's work acknowledges and exemplifies all these possibilities. He sees each human being as 'the focus of a universe' (*Wood*, 30). It will be recalled that his wonderful account, in *Far from the Madding Crowd*, of the world's journey among the stars concludes with a reminder 'that the consciousness of such majestic speeding is derived from a tiny human frame' (14). This realization is everywhere implied in his work – as tacitly, for example, in the poem 'Waiting Both':

> A star looks down at me,
> And says: 'Here I and you
> Stand, each in our degree:
> What do you mean to do, –
> Mean to do?'

> I say: 'For all I know,
> Wait, and let Time go by,
> Till my change come.' – 'Just so,'
> The star says: 'So mean I: –
> So mean I.'

Against convention it is ostensibly the star which opens the conversation, but the 'dialogue' is of course elliptical, a matter of projection. The star knows nothing of mankind or of anything else; it is the human protagonist who gives the star a voice, who does all the talking and all the thinking. The man includes the star; the star does not include the man. Only by the watcher is mere multi-millennial durability perceived as Job-like constancy, prompting the train of thought which is presented as dialogue.

Condemned, as the sole self-conscious species, to collective solipsism, we are compelled to impose our own meanings and evaluations on what we experience:

> At times her whimsical fancy would intensify natural processes around her till they seemed a part of her own story. Rather they became a part of it; for the world is only a psychological phenomenon, and what they seemed they were. (*Tess*, 91)

What is true for Tess is true for everyone. None of us can remove the subjective spectacles through which we view the world. Viewed otherwise, indeed, it could have no meaning. Hardy everywhere shows his awareness that, in George Levine's words, 'Value is human; it does not inhere in nature'.[9] Moreover the values we impose will be incorrigibly personal. Pierston, as has been mentioned, demonstrates as much when he sees in the distance the 'dot of a figure' which he recognizes 'rather by its motion than by its shape' to be the second Avice:

> How incomparably the immaterial dream dwarfed the grandest of substantial things, when here, between those three sublimities – the sky, the rock, and the ocean – the minute personality of this washer-girl filled his consciousness to its extremest boundary, and the stupendous inanimate scene shrank to a corner therein.

It is characteristic of Hardy's intermittent prescience that he perfectly anticipates a metaphor only lately made available by the personal computer. The formulation involves another paradox central to his art. The 'consciousness' that registers our status as 'dots' can simultaneously dismiss the valuation which that status would seem to imply. In 'At Castle Boterel' Hardy recalls climbing a hill with Emma in their courting days, forty years earlier:

> What we did as we climbed, and what we talked of
>   Matters not much, nor to what it led, –
> Something that life will not be balked of
>   Without rude reason till hope is dead,
>   And feeling fled.
>
> It filled but a minute. But was there ever
>   A time of such quality, since or before,
> In that hill's story? To one mind never,
>   Though it has been climbed, foot-swift, foot-sore,
>   By thousands more.
>
> Primaeval rocks form the road's steep border,
>   And much have they faced there, first and last,
> Of the transitory in Earth's long order;
>   But what they recall in colour and cast
>   Is – that we two passed.

The ancient hill has no intrinsic meaning or value. Each of the transients who climbed the slope will have had an individual view of it. For

Hardy this 'primaeval' scene, like the pond in 'Neutral Tones', distils a private memory, a personal emotion to set against the loss imposed by 'Time's unflinching rigour'. What the hill seems to him, it is.

When Hardy claims, in the Preface to *Jude*, that like his other novels it is 'an endeavour to give shape and coherence to a series of seemings' he is reasserting this view of experience. We are obliged to construct our separate realities on the basis of the 'seemings' that chance and personal response supply. This belief goes far towards explaining and justifying the extreme emphasis on the visual in Hardy. To consider how the world 'appears' to someone is, of course, to go beyond mere 'seeing', but the latter process offers a relevant illustrative model.

Hardy has many a comment to make on the psychology of seeing:

> Every woman who makes a permanent impression on a man is usually recalled to his mind's eye as she appeared in one particular scene, which seems ordained to be her special form of manifestation throughout the pages of his memory. (*PBE*, 22)

As an earlier chapter recalled, Hardy's heroines are characteristically mobile, 'flexuous'. Yet in defiance of this plurality he regularly sketches the kind of 'permanent impression' described above. Fancy Day is one of many Hardy heroines to be seen by her lover standing at a window:

> Remaining steady for an instant, the blind went upward from before it, revealing to thirty concentrated eyes: – a young girl framed as a picture by the window architrave, and unconsciously illuminating her countenance to a vivid brightness by a candle she held in her left hand, close to her face; her right hand being extended to the side of the window. She was wrapped in a white robe of some kind, whilst down her shoulders fell a twining profusion of marvellously rich hair in a wild disorder which proclaimed it to be only during the invisible hours of the night that such a condition was discoverable. (*UGT*, 34)

Several times in his fiction Hardy emphasises the difficulty of conveying the complexities of appearance (to say nothing of temperament and character) in a single pen-portrait. In fact he prefaces his very first attempt in this kind – the introduction to Cytherea, in *Desperate Remedies* – with just such a caveat:

> But to attempt to gain a view of her – or indeed of any fascinating woman – from a measured category, is as difficult as to appreciate

the effect of a landscape by exploring it at night with a lantern – or of a full chord of music by piping the notes in succession. (45)

But for workaday purposes of thinking and remembering, a plurality of impressions *must* be fused into some fixed image, if necessarily of an approximate kind. Dick Dewy falls in love on the spot at his first sighting of Fancy at her window. By inference this intimate tableau, with the romantic lighting, the white robe and the tumbling hair will be for him 'her special form of manifestation'. Utterly characteristic of Hardy, of course, is the phrase 'framed as a picture by the window architrave'. Windows, together with peepholes of all kinds, feature so frequently in his work as to have prompted a great deal of speculation about possible voyeuristic tendencies. On the whole I've found such discussion of limited interest, since there are more obvious reasons than psychosexual ones for his resort to this device. His love of paintings makes it natural for him to take pleasure in describing a scene which is framed, composed, carefully lit. As suggested above, what is seen through the window is a conveniently summarized, simplified, perhaps idealized manifestation of a diverse personality: this is how we process experience. Less obviously the idea holds roughly true in those numerous – and manifestly non-voyeuristic – cases in which the view is from the inside rather than from the outside. What is framed by the window can seem a summation, a defining reality. In *The Woodlanders* John South looks out obsessively at the tree which he thinks will bring about his death – as it eventually does. Fitzpiers sees through a window the 'cold and colourless' scene of some woodmen carrying away 'a large limb' snapped from a beech – a sight which makes him exclaim 'My good God! This is life!' (*Wood*, 166). Grace, from Giles's hut, watches more trees 'wrestling for existence, their branches disfigured with wounds resulting from their mutual rubbings and blows' (234). In literal terms these three individuals are all simply looking at trees. In each case, however, what is framed in the window is in effect a view of life, a temporarily dominant 'seeming'.

When Henchard, in *The Mayor of Casterbridge*, receives an unexpected letter from his former lover, Lucetta, 'He took it up in his hands and looked at it as at a picture, a vision, a vista of past enactments' (117). Finding a letter left by his late wife – the letter which reveals that he is not Elizabeth-Jane's father – he regards it 'as if it were a window pane through which he saw for miles' (126). In the Hardy context the comparisons aren't surprising. The rectangular letter, like a rectangular window or picture, offers a framed statement, a fixed view, which the mind must assimilate or resist. Letter or view is a type of the 'seem-ing', the two-dimensional reading into which we render the multiplici-ties we observe. By extension everything that we perceive is in some sense framed by the limitations of our observation and receptivity. Such subjective interpretations furnish, in Hardy's own metaphor, the pages of memory. In a metaphor not available to him they can be seen as a set of static transparencies linked to form the moving picture which constitutes our apprehension of life.

It is easy to belittle man's visual or sensual impressions, circum-scribed and partial as they must inevitably be – a pitiful skimming of the full range of available possibilities. But there is something factitious in this modesty. Who or what does better – or indeed achieves remotely as much? Somehow, after all, we find or impose meanings. It could be proclaimed as a great human achievement that every such 'seeming' in one's private series arrests time and snatches pattern from confusion, as does the Constable painting or the Rosso sculpture. The comparison can be carried a stage further, with *The Leaping Horse* again a useful focus for discussion. The work is a display of reciprocities. Some of those within the painting have already been discussed; there are others which go beyond it. Constable has confronted a landscape vibrant with life and has responded to that vibrancy. He has expanded to meet it – he has been up to it. Moreover he has found the composi-tional and technical means to re-express in oil paint not merely the sights but at least some of the forces to which he has responded. As was suggested above, that creative energy may itself be seen as an equiva-lent to, or an extension of, the very energies he is portraying. The force he depicts is manifested also in the very depiction. Seen in this light Man is no humble observer of mighty external powers: he has corre-sponding powers of his own. The world is remarkable – and so is the mind of man.

Graham-Dixon's suggestion that the 'picture of physical struggle... becomes an analogue for the painter's own imaginative struggle'[10] shows how the case may be reformulated – indeed, turned inside-out. So far from being dwarfed or overawed by the great forces around us we adapt them for our own purposes, annex them as terms of compari-son for our inner dramas.

All these observations may be applied to Hardy. He presents his pow-erful landscapes with a congruent energy of observation, rhythm and verbal definition. The mind and imagination that can dramatize, for example, the phenomenon of the Cliff without a Name, are phenom-ena in their own right. Moreover, as possibly in the case of *The Leaping*

Horse, the great scene evoked can be essentially a mental landscape. In *Far from the Madding Crowd* the moon, the snow, the dark skies, the strange sunrise, the muffled sounds, the frozen footprints of the birds are all invoked to define Boldwood's troubled, brooding, shifting, uncertain, ominous cast of mind. The world we inhabit offers a metaphorical frame of reference for our passions. We shape and proportion them in terms of dramatic physical realities, scaling romantic heights or enduring tempests of grief. All the complexities and intensities of the world without are invoked to dramatize the equivalent complexities and intensities of the world within. In containing the universe the mind becomes a universe.

V

If this book, and this chapter in particular, have seemed to present a confusing account of see-saw argument, of circular or mutually qualifying positions, they have been true to the sustained instabilities of the view of life presented in Hardy's fiction. As a step towards clarification it might be helpful at this point to recapitulate in summary form some of these contradictions or seeming-contradictions.

> ...there was only the imperturbable countenance of the heath, which, having defied the cataclysmal onsets of centuries, reduced to insignificance by its seamed and antique features the wildest turmoil of a single man. (*RN*, 327)

Everywhere in Hardy we find this emphasis on the brevity and triviality of the individual human life, particularly in the context of the apparently changeless features of nature. Yet his descriptive technique bristles with reminders that we cannot pursue our daily lives without turning our backs on this larger view. Repeatedly he will cut from the vast or the ancient to some particular human predicament or an aspect of it. The immense tour through the millennia, when Knight is eye to eye with the trilobite, gives way to the one-line paragraph: 'However, Knight still clung to the cliff' (*PBE*, 210). In the seduction scene in *Tess* Hardy shows us both 'the primeval yews and and oaks of The Chase' and the tears on Tess's eyelashes (77). Though he considers both scales he knows that his story must operate within the smaller one, ostensibly belittled.

More fundamentally, he knows that the larger scale is in any case a figment of our own devising, an expression of relativity. The claimed 'imperturbability' of the heath, for example, is not a daunting fact but a romanticized truism: by definition the heath knows and feels nothing, is incapable of 'turmoil'. On the one hand the universe is infinitely too vast for our minds and our senses to take in. On the other it is only through our minds and our senses that we know this to be the case. We alone are capable of any degree of apprehension of this vastness. Indeed effectively the universe only exists as perceived by our eyes and registered by our brains. The landscape which dwarfs Clym is a landscape contained and defined by his own brain. This duality of view offers no resting place. Not only does solipsism become the obverse of abjection: the capacities producing the sense of abjection conduce to solipsism. Man is miraculously unique in his very potentiality for self-deprecation and self-denigration.

Another paradox: what energizes is what destroys. We die of living. The ageing Jocelyn Pierston views in the mirror his wasting face, and ruefully concludes ' "You cannot live your life and keep it" ' (*W-B*, 160). But the novels assert again and again that to live, to fully live and love, is the great and desirable objective, however wearing or destructive the consequences. Intensity is said to be incompatible with longevity, but it is shown to be incommensurate with it. As Hardy's heroes and heroines burn themselves out, so they proclaim themselves. Jude dies in reiterating the bitter lamentation of Job; Michael Henchard's defining, defiant signature cancels out the attempted self-annihilation of his Will. These men have died of being themselves, of living out their personalities to the full. Hardy celebrates that achievement, and we celebrate it with him.

It is this paradox which allows his vision of endless change and dissolution, of Man's 'bare equality with, and no superiority to, a single entity under the sky' (*DR*, 252), to accommodate and even to enhance the dramatization of human individuality. The leverage of human intelligence, self-consciousness and feeling enables a private drama to outweigh the untold forces of nescience. Hardy's fiction contains many scenes (most notably in *The Return of the Native*) in which an individual is displayed in terms of brief flashes of light in a world of black night:

As Eustacia crossed the fire-beams she appeared for an instant as distinct as a figure in a phantasmagoria – a creature of light surrounded by an area of darkness: the moment passed, and she was absorbed in night again. (*RN*, 354)

The recurring metaphor is a powerful one, but is not merely powerfully pessimistic. The emphasis is reversible. As in the case of Hardy's illuminated insects, 'briefly glorified', the darkness intensifies the transforming light. The moment, in *Far from the Madding Crowd*, when Bathsheba first sees Troy illustrates the point. His spur has caught in her skirt, and he opens her dark lantern to see how to free her:

> A hand seized the lantern, the door was opened, the rays burst out from their prison, and Bathsheba beheld her position with astonishment.
> The man to whom she was hooked was brilliant in brass and scarlet. He was a soldier. His sudden appearance was to darkness what the sound of a trumpet is to silence. (*FMC*, 171)

The 'brilliance', the shock, are perfectly proportioned to the ensuing response which will rouse her personality to passion and commitment, bring her fully to life – 'irradiate' her, to use a favourite Hardy term. Elsewhere in the Wessex novels, of course, this intensifying effect can extend beyond strength of passion to force or grandeur of conduct. There seems general critical agreement that Henchard is in traditional terms Hardy's nearest approach to a Tragic Hero. Yet he is placed in a setting where there is reminder after reminder of the brevity and triviality of human life – in a town which announces 'old Rome in every street, alley, and precinct' (*MC*, 70), a town where Roman skeletons are regularly dug up, a town which speaks of countless forgotten generations. For all Henchard's 'character' he, too, will die forgotten, and, like his timid wife's, his 'wishes and ways will all be as nothing!' (121). Yet his perpendicular presence, his pride, his will, his energy, his anger, his commitment, his dominance, his instinct for justice loom unforgettably from the novel. The light he burns with compels our attention, and we forget the surrounding darkness. If he is an exceptional person, the same novel offers an equally revealing humble one. Elizabeth-Jane and Farfrae, in their search for the missing Henchard, scour Egdon, 'that ancient country whose surface never had been stirred to a finger's depth, save by the scratchings of rabbits, since brushed by the feet of the earliest tribes' (330). The tumuli these prehistoric peoples have left behind help to give the setting an epic scale, within which the 'solitary human form' of the wretched Abel Whittle seems negligible indeed. Yet Whittle's account of Henchard's death, an account steeped in simple compassion, offers a stark contrast to the impersonality of the landscape, and his instinctive generosity of feeling rebukes the empty sublimity of mere appearances. We admire and endorse that generosity as we admire and endorse Henchard's whole-heartedness, and the fact that we do so implies another continuity to set against the brevity of individual existence, a continuity of moral feeling. Certain primary human values manifestly survive through generations and civilizations. For this reason, too, the vividness of the individual stories in Hardy is not at odds with his vision of transience and perpetual change, but in dialectic with it. Indeed, the case might be put more strongly. Although the novels close with darkness it is the light which has been compelling. The passionate, agonized individuals whose doings Hardy chronicles luminously display, like filaments, energies only darkly latent in nature at large, giving them expression rather as a fading heath-bell may give a voice to the wind.

These tensions and paradoxes in Hardy, these to-and-fro-conflicting contradictions, are themselves an expression of the restless energies central to his theme. Like people, like objects, our ideas dissolve and re-form. We live amid change, we apprehend it, we partake of it. The things we see, the things we hear, all, in their various ways, speak of unending transition. Several times in the course of this book the second chapter of *Far from the Madding Crowd* has been invoked, as involving sights, sounds and motions of various kinds, human and non-human, promiscuously mingled. Dead leaves, grasses, hedges and trees sing in the wind; Gabriel plays his flute; there is the muffled ringing of sheep-bells overgrown with wool. The shepherd moves purposefully among his flock; the wind wanders and flounders; the restless stars throb and soar. They are seen as useful lights – like the lanterns, the candle and the fire in the huts below – as divine constellations, as an enormous timepiece, as 'a work of art superlatively beautiful'. In this night of multiple activities a lamb is born. Elsewhere on the hill is a day-old calf. The hill itself is initially described as indestructible and undisturbable, a solid background, it might seem, for the narrative to come. But frames of reference melt or mutate: within a page or so Hardy depicts the entire globe, of which the hill is but a minute part, making 'stately progress' among the stars. Gabriel admires the vast heavenly panorama within a short time of tending that 'little speck of life' the lamb. He realizes that one light which he has taken to be a star is in fact 'artificial' and close at hand. Within minutes he has turned away from the panorama and is peering through a peephole at the girl who is to shape his future life. A poetic 'seeming' gives way to a personal one. Bathsheba yawns, and Oak yawns in sympathy.

This is the shortest day of the year, traditionally thought of as a dead time, yet everywhere Hardy looks and listens he finds life and movement. The stars seem to be 'but the throbs of one body, timed to a common pulse'. All the various motions within the chapter are in effect timed to that same pulse. An extra dimension of instability is derived from a sense of fluctuating perceptions: the thing seen changes as it comes to be seen differently. One experience fades into another. The chapter is a medley of shifting perspectives and multiple readings. Rather as with a mobile its own nervous motions mimic the motions of living, seeing, thinking, feeling.

This is a particularly concentrated chapter, and in that sense an atyp-ical one, an expanded version of what I have been calling a 'concatena-tion'. Yet a Hardy novel as a whole works very much in this same way, and can and should be so read. Certainly Hardy is inconsistent about the very energies he describes and expresses. In the *Life* he observes:

> It is the on-going – i.e. the 'becoming' – of the world that produces its sadness. If the world stood still at a felicitous moment there would be no sadness in it. (210)

But if the world did stand still, as Chapter II of *Far from the Madding Crowd* implicitly suggests, there would be no life in it: the change *is* the life. In the Preface to *Late Lyrics and Earlier* Hardy insists that poetry, lit-erature in general, and religion 'must like all other things keep moving, becoming...' (*Complete Poems*, 561). In 'A Sign-Seeker' he refers to 'All the vast various moils that mean a world alive'. The very inconsisten-cies noted here, the lapses from one 'seeming' to another, are them-selves manifestations of life, of change, of 'becoming'.

It must be conceded that a reading responsive to such fluctuations necessarily seems at odds with the interest in defined characters and an end-directed story which so much in Hardy's fiction encourages us to feel. But that is part of his point. We all conduct our daily lives at the level of 'story', looking to secure this job, to buy this house, to marry that person. But while these hopes and ambitions come and go most of us have a continuing desire to see our doings as an aspect of some greater pattern. It is instinctive in us to try to relate to the world around us, to apprehend larger powers, to derive feelings from weather or scenery, to read meanings into nature or the stars. For this reason a narrative landscape painting can effortlessly elicit a reciprocal reading: we respond in that instinctive, accustomed way. The figures give con-ceptual focus to the scene, attempting to go somewhere or achieve something; the natural background offers lavish commentary on the human drama. Our attention moves between the two possibilities. Similarly Hardy's novels dramatize that duality of experience, that movement in our minds between the world within us, which is yet an aspect of physical life, and the world without us, which is yet an aspect of our thought.

This mode of writing, of course, relates closely to Modernist attempts to build the limitations of human consciousness and thought into the very structures of art – to incorporate the relativity of experience. Hardy notes in the *Life*, at the end of 1865:

> To insects the twelvemonth has been an epoch, to leaves a life, to tweeting birds a generation, to man a year. (56)

Though we are all evanescent, all subject to ageing and encroachment, we live at different speeds, see along different sight-lines. Man alone, through intellect and imagination, has partial access to alternative modes and scales of vision – an access which dooms him to inconsistencies of thought and conduct. Hardy could quite properly remain unperturbed by his frequent self-contradictions. The concept of 'a series of seemings' specifically allows for them. His more bluntly pessimistic assertions, to the effect that human life is insignificant or that we are better off dead, not merely need not, but should not be taken as his last word. Hardy provides a prophylactic against his own darker utterances. His last word is that there can be no such thing as a last word, even from himself.

Indeed his work inescapably insists that we must live with ambiguities, fluctuation and indeterminacy. We change and the world changes around us. But for Hardy that realization need not imply bewildered submission to mere chaos. Traditions, values, emotions, aspirations are not obliterated, but continually renewed and reasserted in action. The scheme of perpetual motion in which we are trapped displays an underlying form – the form which shapes the movement, as in the case of a fountain.

Does Hardy appear a greater author if read in this spirit? Probably. He should certainly appear a more ambitious, far-seeing, and coherent one. His relative position in some notional canonical league table of novelists is only a side issue. What matters is that his work should be given the full, flexible, multiply-responsive reading which its complex energies deserve.

Notes

Chapter 1   Introduction

1 L. Carroll, *Through the Looking-Glass*, in *The Annotated Alice*, ed. Martin Gardner, revised edn (London: Penguin, 1970), p. 306.
2 See H. Wine, *Claude: the Poetic Landscape*, (London, National Gallery Publications, 1994), p. 9 and *passim*.
3 See L. Parris and I. Fleming-Williams, *Constable*, (London: Tate Gallery Publications), 301ff.
4 Ibid., 302.
5 Ibid., 304.
6 *The Independent*, 18 June 1991. At the time I was writing this book a whole series of the art-reviews written by Andrew Graham-Dixon in *The Independent* seemed to bear on my thinking about Hardy. I found them a great stimulus.
7 J. Bayley, *An Essay on Hardy* (Cambridge, CUP, 1978), pp. 13 and 19.
8 Parris and Fleming, *Constable*, *op cit.*, p. 296.
9 For example the quoted passage features in Chapter LII of *Tess*; the description of an old shepherd at a hiring-fair (p. 175) reappears in *The Mayor of Casterbridge* (p. 161).
10 For comment on Hardy's use of 'liminal imagery', see Barbara Hardy's 'Thresholds and Verges: Hardy Imagines Imagination' in *Tensions and Transitions* (London: Faber and Faber, 1990), ed. M. Irwin, M. Kinkead-Weekes and A. R. Lee, pp. 82–102).
11 See the opening of Chapter XVII of *Oliver Twist*.

Chapter 2   Hardy's Insects

1 R. Gittings, *The Older Hardy* (London: Heinemann, 1978), p. 10.

Chapter 3   Noises in Hardy's Novels

1 J. Grundy, *Hardy and the Sister Arts*, (London: Macmillan, 1979), p. 137.
2 I would apply to this passage, as to a number or others in Hardy, a comment made by Rod Edmond concerning 'Goblin Market': 'Readings of the poem which make literal its metaphors seem inevitably reductive, and yet the suggestiveness of metaphor and its decoding is central to the reading of poetry'. R. Edmond, *Affairs of the Hearth*, (London: Routledge, 1988), p. 185. See the discussion of the passage from *A Laodicean* in Chapter 6, below, for further reflections on this dilemma.
3 In a lecture given at the Eleventh International Hardy Conference, Dorchester, 1994.

Chapter 4   The Poetry of Motion

1 J. Grundy, *Hardy and the Sister Arts* (London: Macmillan, 1979), Chapter 5.
2 The quotations are taken from *The Portable Darwin*, ed. D. M. Porter and P. W. Graham, (London: Penguin, 1993), pp. 371ff.
3 See (e.g.) *Thomas Hardy: the Critical Heritage*, ed. R. G. Cox, (London: Routledge & Kegan Paul, 1970), pp. 40, 47, 51, 71.
4 J. Hillis Miller, *Thomas Hardy, Distance and Desire*, (Cambridge, Mass., and London, 1970), pp. 140 and 144.
5 Ibid., p. 142.

Chapter 5   Erosion, Deformation and Reformation

1 *The Portable Darwin*, p. 148.
2 See M. Millgate, *Thomas Hardy: A Biography*, (Oxford: Oxford University Press, 1982), p. 316.
3 See (e.g.) *The Independent*, Monday, 11 July 1988, p. 6.

Chapter 6   Concatenations

1 *Sense and Sensibility*, Chapter Nine.
2 Ibid., Chapter Forty-two.
3 C. Brontë, *Villette*, Chapter 21.
4 G. Eliot, *Middlemarch*, Chapter 20.
5 *Peeping Tom* (First published London: Chatto & Windus, 1984; Black Swan pb. edition, 1985, p. 241.
6 In a lecture '*The Well-Beloved*: A Modernist Experiment?', delivered on 13 April 1997, at the 'Portland Weekend' organized by the Thomas Hardy Society to mark the centenary of that novel.
7 D. Lodge, *The Language of Fiction*, (London: Routledge & Kegan Paul, 1966), p. 187.
8 Ibid., p. 182.
9 I. Gregor, *The Great Web*, (London: Faber and Faber, 1974), p. 188.
10 See above, page 12 and related note. Chapters LI and LII of *Tess* feature borrowings from 'The Dorsetshire Labourer'; Chapter II draws on Hardy's 'Unsigned Review' of Barnes's *Poems of Rural Life in the Dorset Dialect* (*Personal Writings*, pp. 94ff.)

Chapter 7   'This insubstantial pageant'

1 'Charles Dickens', in G. Orwell, *The Collected Essays, Journalism and Letters*, ed. Sonia Orwell and Ian Angus, (London: Secker & Warburg, second impression, 1968), vol. I, p. 454.
2 L. Parris and I. Fleming-Williams, *Constable* (London: Tate Gallery Publications), p. 297.
3 *The Independent*, Tuesday, 24 March 1992, p. 18.
4 *The Independent*, Tuesday, 11 June 1993, p. 14.

5 *The Independent*, Tuesday, 1 March 1994, p. 23.
6 See Robert Gittings, *Young Thomas Hardy*, (London, Heinemann, 1975), p. 50.
7 J. Hillis Miller, *Thomas Hardy, Distance and Desire* (Cambridge, Mass., and London, 1970), p. 87.
8 G. Beer, *Darwin's Plots: evolutionary theory in Darwin, George Eliot and nineteenth-century fiction* (Routledge & Kegan Paul, 1983), pp. 248–9.
9 G. Levine, *The Realistic Imagination*, (Chicago and London, University of Chicago Press, 1981), page 235.
10 *The Independent*, Tuesday, 18 June, 1991.

Index